The Community College of Kent

69000

Also by Dr Hilary Jones

Before You Call The Doctor
Your Child's Health

I'M TOO BUSY TO BE STRESSED

How to Recognise and Relieve the Symptoms of Stress

Dr Hilary Jones

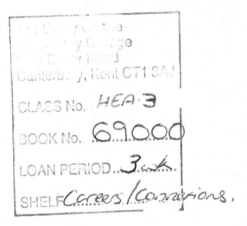
Hodder & Stoughton

First published in Great Britain in 1997 by Hodder & Stoughton
A division of Hodder Headline PLC

10 9 8 7 6 5 4 3 2 1

This book is intended as a guide to people who want to improve and
maintain their health. If you are concerned in any way about your health,
you should seek medical advice.

British Library Cataloguing in Publication Data

Jones, Hilary
I'm too busy to be stressed
1. Stress (Psychology) 2. Stress Management
I.Title
155.9'042

ISBN 0 340 67231 5

Typeset by Hewer Text Composition Services, Edinburgh
Printed and bound in Great Britain by
Cox and Wyman Ltd, Reading

Hodder and Stoughton
A Division of Hodder Headline PLC
338 Euston Road
London NW1 3BH

To my parents Evan and Noreen

CONTENTS

ACKNOWLEDGEMENTS

I would like to thank all of my patients who over the years have proved just how universal the symptoms of stress really are, and how ridiculously often the true underlying cause goes completely unrecognized. In addition they have confirmed which solutions and remedies for stress actually work, and so have been particularly invaluable in compiling the second half of this book.

I should like to thank Jeremy King, my producer at GMTV, for his help in soberly researching the subject, and both Jane Ledger and Glenys Whiley without whose expertise on the word processor the manuscript would never have been completed in time.

Sarah, my wife, was as always enormously helpful and supportive, as were Aden and Sharon Curran who must qualify as by far the least stressed people I know.

Figure 16 on page 71 was reprinted by permission of the publisher from Holmes and Rahe Social Readjustment Scale, Journal of Psychosomatic Research Vol. 11, No. 2, pp. 213–218. Copyright 1967 by Elsevier Science Inc.

FOREWORD

I like the title of this book because it conveys exactly the thinking of those people most resistant to helping themselves. Yet 'stress' is not simply a fact of life – something which must be stoically accepted and endured. Unless we do something about it, its effects can creep up on us unnoticed, while we remain quite unaware that many of the problems we face in life are simply the result of our response to pressure and strain.

This book not only makes us more conscious of the connection between stress and symptoms, but it also empowers us to break the vicious cycle which can ruin the quality of our lives, and spoil our ability to enjoy ourselves.

What appeals to me most about this book, however, is its relevance to *all* of us. Not just to the archetypal hard-driving executives, but to their long-suffering subordinates, as well as to harassed housewives, single parents, the unemployed, and to those faced with redundancy, retirement and ill-health.

Dr Hilary Jones shows us how we can find ways to climb out of the holes we may have dug for ourselves and move towards a more relaxed, successful and fulfilling future. And his ideas are not just based on fashionable academic theory; he has combined the lessons of his 22 years in medical practice to compile a sensible, practical and effective solution to the problems of modern-day stress.

A lot of us can harbour a death-wish beneath our 'I'm too busy to be stressed' facade. If so, we ignore this book at our peril.

INTRODUCTION

I have not spent the last twenty years as a doctor, with all the urgency and responsibility which that job entails, without learning something about handling pressure, nor appreciating the consequences of relentless and unremitting strain on the thousands of patients I have treated and the numerous colleagues with whom I have worked. Live television presenting, involving broadcasting and writing for large audiences within strictly defined deadlines and legal confines, also throws up its own particular challenges, as does being a dad to five wonderful but demanding offspring.

What I have learned during that time is that there is a huge amount that can be done to alleviate unpleasant stress, and even to turn it to your advantage, but despite the current abundance of stress management courses now available, entrenched, die-hard attitudes towards the subject still remain. There is, for example, an enduring but completely erroneous attitude that stress is an inevitable part of achievement and success and that you cannot have one without the other. There is the belief that 'when the going gets tough, the tough get going' and that part of this resilience necessarily means being edgy, tense and wound up. It is also tempting to believe that if you really want a job to be done well then you should ask a really busy person to do it.

But too much stress turns people into monsters. It makes them act out of character, or may even change their personality altogether. It makes them lose sight of the very things in life for which they are striving, and it makes them forget how and why they are trying to achieve them. Taken to its extreme, excessive stress can ruin people's lives, and the lives of the people around them too.

'I'm Too Busy to be Stressed'

Can't you just imagine someone you know very well saying, 'I'm too busy to be stressed'? You can picture them in your mind's eye, someone who is so fired up, so overstretched and so 'wired' that the prospect of them ever being prepared to slow down is extremely remote.

It was Mark, a thirty-five-year-old television producer I once worked with, who originally coined the phrase 'I'm too busy to be stressed'. He was always behind with his deadlines, rushing around ineffectually and getting ratty with everyone as a result. I knew he suffered from stomach ulcers, irritable bowel syndrome and palpitations because he never could find time to see his own doctor and often resorted to consulting me in the corridor as he rushed past. One particular morning his girlfriend had given him an ultimatum concerning their relationship. His job, too, was on the line because he had screwed up on collecting some urgent video footage from another studio. Unfortunately I was blissfully unaware of this when I put my head round the door to inform him that the stress management course the boss had organised for the staff was just about to begin. He had a telephone braced between an ear and a shoulder, one hand operated a computer keyboard, the other held a cigarette, and at the same time he was re-running a videotape in a playback machine in front of him. His head shot up towards me as his face went purple with frustration and rage.

'Don't be bloody silly,' he said, 'I'm far too busy to be stressed. Besides I'm late enough already!' His remarks went down a treat on the course, and even he could see the funny side of it two years later when he had successfully come out of therapy. But joking apart, we all know lots of people like Mark. Perhaps if you are really honest, you can see that one of those people, at least part of the time, is you. Try completing the 'How Stressed are You?' questionnaire at the end of this introduction on page 5 to get the true picture.

All of us suffer from excess stress now and again. And I say suffer, because the symptoms which stress can provoke can be very unpleasant indeed. Most of us have lain awake tossing and turning and unable to sleep because of unresolved things 'going round' in our minds. Most of us have snapped at the very people who in reality least deserve it. Few of us have never done anything in the heat of the moment which we later regret. And all of us could accomplish more in less time, yet remain calmer, healthier and happier if only we could learn to handle stress more effectively. The truth is that too much stress for too long for any one individual can cause social, emotional, psychological and physical problems which can have far-reaching consequences for the sufferer, their family, their friends and their work colleagues.

Doctors, of all people, should know this. Not only do they see the dreadful side-effects of stress in their patients, but their own workload, responsibilities and long hours make them prime candidates themselves for extreme stress, burn-out, alcoholism, divorce and even suicide. Ironically, and perhaps hypocritically, this profession which is probably best equipped to recognise and deal with stress in others, is also the worst at recognising it in themselves. Indeed, it has always been said that doctors make the worst patients. When 2000 GPs were recently invited to attend a stress-relieving course in Glasgow as part of their postgraduate education, and for which they are actually paid, only four could find time to come. That is only 0.0002% of GPs who were not 'too busy to suffer from stress'.

If GPs themselves, with all the literature and practical advice available to them, are neglecting the effects of stress, what chance can there be for everyone else? How can we ever learn to come to terms with impatience, rage, relationship problems, insomnia and tension? And how can we ever stave off the stress-induced ravages that rising blood pressure, silently advancing heart disease and damaged immunity can cause? Excessive stress contributes to almost every serious ailment known to man, including cancer, arthritis, heart attacks and mental illness. Yet not all stress is bad. Without any stress at all in our lives, the world would be a very dull place. How weary, stale, flat and unprofitable it would all seem. The trick is to find the right stress balance. Not too much and not too little, just the right amount.

Stress is not an immutable fact of life from which there is no escape. There are practical and effective solutions. This book is designed to help you discover that elusive formula for achieving the correct stress balance – a degree of stress that is enough to help you work efficiently and effectively, even when the pressure is on, yet not so great that your performance deteriorates and your physical and emotional well-being suffer. It is a book in which I have deliberately avoided the scientific jargon and stress-speak of the behavioural psychologists and the stress counsellors. I hope it will be every bit as useful to the frantic housewife as the driven executive, and every bit as practical for the over-burdened secretary and the hard-up unemployed. It is for the bored factory worker, the high-flying managing director, the bereaved, the lovelorn, the divorced and the sick. It is for the young and the old, the rich and the poor. For anyone in fact who wants to lead a more relaxed, healthier and happier life but so far has not had the time to find out quite how to achieve it. It is an ideal book in fact for anyone who has ever thought themselves 'too busy to be stressed'.

Questionnaire:
How Stressed Are You?

		Always	Sometimes	Never
		3	2	1
1	I underestimate how long it takes to do things			
2	I tend to be late for appointments			
3	I nod or butt in when people speak slowly			
4	Queuing makes me angry and irritated			
5	I often take on more than one job at a time			
6	I skip meals, or eat rapidly or on the run			
7	I walk briskly rather than stroll			
8	I know I drive faster than I should			
9	Trivial things easily irritate me			
10	I get angry with myself if I make mistakes			
11	I find fault and criticise others rather than praising them			
12	However tired I am, my mind is always busy and I lie awake at night worrying			
13	I will do a job myself to ensure it is done properly			
14	I find it hard to make important decisions			
15	I drink alcohol most days			
16	I deny or ignore problems in the hope they will go away			
17	If something or someone really annoys me I tend to bottle it up			
18	When I play sport or games I really try to win			
19	I strive for perfection			
20	I avoid keeping count of all the major problems I face			

Self-assessment
Add up your score as follows:

   Score 3 every time you answer 'Always'.
   Score 2 every time you answer 'Sometimes'.
   Score 1 every time you answer 'Never'.

20–30 points
You are generally fairly laid-back and calm. Consider whether a little more of a challenge in your life might prove motivational and help you progress your ambitions.

31–45 points
You have achieved a reasonable balance of stress factors. At times, when the balance tips the wrong way, you will need to make adjustments.

46–60 points
You are highly susceptible to stress. Despite working very hard, you achieve little. You are 'too busy to be stressed' – or so you think! Read on.

CHAPTER ONE

STRESS IN TODAY'S CRAZY WORLD

Despite its potential for progress through understanding, co-operation and love, this is an increasingly overcrowded world facing more competition, selfishness, and hostility at every turn. The pace of life as the new millennium approaches has become ever faster and more fraught. Everywhere we look, we seem to find yet more sources of stress. It has become part of the fabric of modern existence. It is now something we live and breathe.

As a GP, I see the effects of excess stress in my surgery on a daily if not hourly basis. I see high blood pressure, heart attacks, panic attacks and depression. I see irritable bowel syndrome, insomnia and migraine. I even see relatively new conditions, affecting adults and children alike, which are inextricably bound up with stress. Almost every patient who consults me is suffering from a condition that is, at least in part, exacerbated by the pressures, tensions and hassles of daily existence. Even the fifty percent of people who do not acknowledge it in research surveys are detrimentally affected by subconscious stress. David, aged forty-one, was a typical example.

When Stress is Ignored

I was called to David's house by his wife because he had had chest pain that morning. I had been treating her for depression and insomnia, and I knew him only vaguely. He did not attend the surgery very often, and whenever I had seen him, he'd always seemed dismissive of his wife's symptoms and irritable, as if the whole business was a bit of a waste of his precious time. He was overweight, but happy to be so, and worked for a successful computer company that was going places. It afforded him a lavish lifestyle including a top-of-the-range Porsche of which he was particularly proud.

When I arrived at the house David was tucked up in bed, sweating profusely. The thought that he had had a heart attack had obviously occurred to both of us. He was breathing rapidly in short shallow breaths, he was tensed up, clammy to the touch, nauseous and very, very frightened. His pulse was rapid, but his heart sounded normal and there was nothing to suggest any problem with his lungs. I took his temperature and a sample of blood, and carried out an ECG, an electrical recording of his heartbeat. Everything was normal. As I sat there and chatted, his breathing slowed down, his heart rate settled and the feeling of sickness abated. In due course the blood tests, which might have proved a heart attack had taken place, also came back normal.

David had in fact had his first ever anxiety attack. He vigorously denied it for a while, and tried to pretend that all was well by throwing himself back into his work with a vengeance. But he finally had to admit defeat when he was unable to continue during a sales presentation at the office. He'd also forgotten two important appointments and had physically assaulted his wife over some trivial domestic matter, causing her to leave home with the children until he sorted himself out.

Talking it through made him become slowly aware of a whole catalogue of problems, worries and concerns which he had been ignoring or denying for a considerable period of time. His family had suffered, and so too had his health and his career. Yet just like thousands of others in a similar situation, he had been totally unaware how vulnerable he had become to the effects of prolonged stress.

The Stress Epidemic

It is obvious that work is a potent source of stress. But so too, these days, is just travelling to and from your place of employment. Overcrowded public transport, traffic queues and expensive or unavailable parking make people's blood boil. Recent cases of road rage attacks and car-jackings have done nothing to improve our sense of personal security. Arguments, separations and other domestic difficulties are reflected in a soaring divorce rate and promote untold misery and unhappiness for millions. Even those families who are lucky enough still to be intact, spend less and less time sharing their busy lives together.

Far too many of us, whether willingly or unwillingly, have become part of the rat race and forgotten what it is we are working for. Most of us in modern Britain are living to work, rather than working to live. Despite that, there is an all-pervading and constant fear of redundancy. With nearly three million jobless, and an increased tendency in the workplace towards short-term contracts, these fears are entirely understandable. More people are in debt than ever before, and the number of home repossessions taking place as a result of people falling behind with their mortgage repayments gets larger year by year. On top of all the traditional stresses which cannot be predicted, such as illness, bereavement and disability, there are all the frustrations which the modern world has foisted upon us. The new technology that was supposed to provide us with extra leisure time, longer lives and prosperity, has in fact put further strain upon us and made our working week even longer. Faxes, personal computers, electronic mail and cellular phones have, if anything, accelerated the pace of life and increased, rather than decreased, the pressures we are expected to handle. There is an entire generation of people like myself, who are forced to learn this new language and new way of life before we can even begin to face the challenges of a brave new world and lifestyle.

Added to all these factors are irritations that most of us have to face at some time or another – moving house, retirement, sexual problems, legal actions, rows with the in-laws, the responsibilities of parenthood, noise pollution, and holidays which go wrong. It is little wonder that stress in today's crazy world is considered to be of epidemic proportions.

But Hasn't Life Always Been Stressful?

Is stress however, just a twentieth-century phenomenon as so many people believe? Surely, the human race has experienced much worse stress in years gone by? Neanderthal man did not have to suffer the hell of queueing at the supermarket checkout, but when he went hunting for food he was not even sure if he would return home at all.

Christians thrown to the lions in the arena of the Colosseum in ancient Rome must have known what it was like to have suffered from stress, and the civilisations that existed before the relatively stable society of today had to live with the constant threat of war, famine and plague. It was surely worse to have been on the dole in the 1930s than it is to be on income support at the present time? There was no answer to the spectre of tuberculosis in times gone by, when life expectancy was less than half what it is today and a high proportion of children died before their fifth birthday. All in all, any talk of stress in today's world, when we have more disposable income than ever before, a vast number of material goods at our disposal, better health care and far-reaching choices, sounds more like whinging than anything else. But stress is relative, and a great deal has to do with our expectations.

We do not expect to experience death from infectious disease nowadays because we feel we should be protected by vaccination and antibiotics. There is shock when we are on the receiving end of violence, because there should be no place for it in a civilised and sophisticated society. In fact, it is *because* we take so very much for granted that we feel stressed when the smooth running of the machine is upset. When we lose control of our environment, and when the things that bug us become increasingly frequent, intense and prolonged, that is when we become stressed.

In the past, the threats to our lives were more physical than they are today. These days the threats are more psychological in origin. They are threats to our self-esteem and our security. They are challenges to our role in society and to our relationships with those around us. We are bombarded with rapid and never ending change, with trivial frustrations and forced social interactions. Circumstances force many of us to work even when we feel our families really need us at home to give them the love and support that they deserve.

Many traditional support systems have been eroded or have disappeared entirely. Communities which were once small enough to look after all their members' interests have become simply too big to provide the same support. Far from feeling part of their community, the majority of people these days feel isolated and vulnerable. The extended family that once existed here, and still exists in many under-developed countries, formed a support system that we used to rely on. Family businesses were handed down from generation to generation, traditions in how to raise the children and keep them healthy were taught by grandparents to their offspring, and when the chips were down, the family were always there. For the most part that has changed.

Lastly, but by no means least, our population is far less physically active than it ever was in the past. Our children currently exhibit frighteningly low levels of fitness. Mechanisation has meant that fewer adults are involved in performing physical jobs now. Factory and office workers are more likely to drive to work then take the lift, rather than walking and using the stairs these days. The basic problem is that all the changes within us which prepare us for the famous 'fight or flight reaction' – the physiological stress response – are supposed to be dissipated through physical means. But, fortunately, we seldom need to resort to coming to blows with the boss, or running like hell from awkward situations we encounter at work. What happens instead is, we become impatient, irritated or angry. All the stresses of modern life commit us to a state of high alertness which cannot be offset by physical action and muscular exertion. Instead, the tension and stress within us insidiously accumulate and begin to take their toll on our health.

The chemical and hormonal changes which affect every single organ of our body when we are stressed, have not evolved along with modern civilisation. The very biological system that is designed to protect us from external threat has become our number one killer, with an increased mortality rate from heart disease, mental illness, cancer and a host of disabling and degenerative conditions. Civilisation and the advantages which accompany it certainly come at a price.

CHAPTER TWO

WHAT DOES STRESS REALLY MEAN?

I am quite sure everyone knows what they mean by 'stress'. When you are tearing your hair out, rushing around like a headless chicken with your heart beating fit to burst, you are quite sure you already know what stress is, thank you very much! It is pressure, it is tension, it is anxiety and frustration all rolled into one, and it is something that most people could well do without.

But although stress can be all of these unpleasant emotions and feelings, it is also a lot more besides. In fact, stress is not necessarily unpleasant at all. Many people thrive on the buzz they get from meeting exciting new challenges. They only work effectively with a deadline to beat, or when they are juggling with several different jobs at once. An athlete in competition or a performer on stage will rise to the big occasion and surpass themselves, even in front of a critical audience. This is equal to the stressful thrill that young people actually pay for when they subject themselves to the exhilaration of the 'Black Hole' roller coaster ride at the fairground, or the horror of a particularly gruesome suspense thriller at the movies. The adrenalin rush they experience is second to none. For them, stress is a good thing, a positive, motivating and stimulating force without which life would be dull and unexciting.

How you respond to these different types of stress depends very largely on your personality. Some people seem to lap up challenges and are simply not content without them, whereas others feel acutely uncomfortable if they are pushed faster than their customary pace allows, or asked to perform yet another task before the previous one is finished. Some individuals even choose to put themselves under increased pressure by deliberately taking on more than they can realistically handle. For whatever reason, they believe that to truly achieve they must drive themselves ever harder and more furiously.

The Definition of Stress

The word 'stress' was originally derived from the Latin 'stringere' meaning 'to draw tight' and in the past the word was used to describe hardship, suffering or disease.

Cary Cooper, Professor of Organisational Psychology at the University of Manchester Institute of Science and Technology (UMIST) admits stress is an umbrella word which is used in various contexts to describe different causes and a range of different responses. But the underlying meaning is the same and some kind of working definition of stress can be useful if it takes account of the different personality types, the varying demands made upon each individual, and how their subsequent responses may differ.

Hans Selye, the founder of modern research into stress has defined it simply as 'the role of wear and tear on the body'. In physical and engineering terms, if you compare the stresses and strains on a bridge to those impinging on human beings, the powerful water currents flowing around the bridge's pillars, and the massive juggernauts thundering across its surface, will eventually erode and weaken it, just as repeated traumas in our everyday lives erode and weaken us. Yet this is not the best possible definition of stress, because unlike the inanimate bridge that cannot move, change or respond, human beings certainly can. We can make adaptations when we are put under strain and, depending on how effectively we do it, we can either succeed or fail. In addition, our personalities determine how we react to stress and our genetic makeup, our upbringing and education all play a part.

Perhaps Richard Lazarus at the University of California has a better definition. His newer and more comprehensive theories on stress emphasise that it 'is a state we experience when the demands that are made upon us cannot be counterbalanced by our ability to deal with them'. It is how we see those demands, and how we feel we can cope with them, that will ultimately decide whether we feel completely overwhelmed at one extreme or bored stiff at the other. There is a middle road, of course, when the demands made upon us are stimulating and our coping resources are perfectly adapted to deal with them. This is a satisfying, rewarding and happy situation to be in, but although many of us will have experienced it from time to time, most of us go through life in a continual state of flux. We stagger from a point where we have far too much to do and too little time to do it in, to having time on our hands to kill, and nothing at all constructive to do with it.

Walking the Stress Tightrope

This balancing of life's demands against our ability to deal with them can be demonstrated by the analogy of a person walking a tightrope, as in the illustration below.

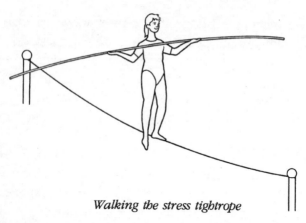

Walking the stress tightrope

Every single one of us walks a tricky 'stress tightrope', the tightrope being the path we take in our journey through each day of our life. There are dangers and pitfalls at every step, but we have travelled the same course hundreds of times before and we are confident and stable as we proceed. Stress is not perceived in this ordinary situation and so we continue to make our steady progress. Sometimes, to break the monotony and test ourselves, we go a little faster or deliberately put up an obstacle in our way. This makes us feel especially good because we have mastered a new challenge and proved something to ourselves at the same time. Problems only arise when situations occur which throw us off balance. For the tightrope walker, those situations can come from different directions. A gusty wind, or driving rain would be awkward. Vibrations or altered tensions in the rope would be problematical. Arthritis in the tightrope walker's ankle joints or, worse still, giddiness or vertigo would seriously threaten their ability to make it to the other side.

Under these kinds of conditions the tightrope walker's confidence, determination and resolve to succeed would be sorely tested, especially if there were no safety net and nobody to catch them if they fell. With our previous experience of such difficulties, any person prone to give up rather easily could falter and fall. A more resilient individual, on the other hand, might fight to the last and stubbornly cling on. A lot depends on personality type and inherent coping skills. The simple truth is that some of us are natural born tightrope walkers and some of us never will be.

Making the job easier for all of us, however, no matter what our natural ability, is the balancing pole. This long, smooth tightrope walker's accessory is a great leveller. Small shifts in balance can be quickly restored by a deftly applied adjustment to the position of the pole. Under normal circumstances the pole wavers just a fraction, up and down on either side, and the tightrope walker is in perfect equilibrium. When external factors weigh down too heavily on either end of the pole, however, the tightrope walker wobbles, over balances and finally takes the plunge.

This model of stress is important as it underpins everything the rest of the book says about how to manage stress and cope with its effects. In the two illustrations below we can see how the tightrope walker might experience different levels of stress depending on the position of the pole, and how any external factors causing difficulty, 'stressors' as we shall call them, bring this about.

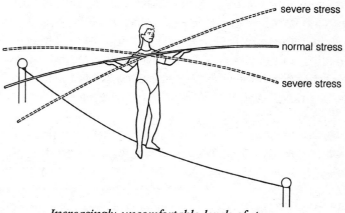

Increasingly uncomfortable levels of stress

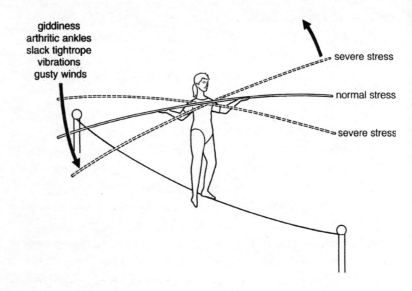

giddiness
arthritic ankles
slack tightrope
vibrations
gusty winds

severe stress

normal stress

severe stress

Increasing demands cause increasing stress

Adverse and unpredictable stresses will swing the tightrope walker's pole alarmingly to one side, putting the tightrope walker under severe and unpleasant stress. The stresses are similar to the demands made upon us each and every day of our lives and they can only be counterbalanced by our ability to respond appropriately to them, as illustrated below. The tightrope walker learns to lean to one side and shift his weight, then he adjusts the position of the pole, perhaps removing his left hand briefly to effectively lighten one end of the pole, changing its centre of gravity and restoring equilibrium. Part of this reaction is intuitive but another part is carefully and painstakingly learned and coached. This is the tightrope walker's coping mechanism, and provided it proves sufficiently effective, normal stress levels will be restored.

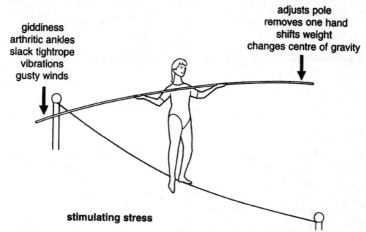

giddiness
arthritic ankles
slack tightrope
vibrations
gusty winds

adjusts pole
removes one hand
shifts weight
changes centre of gravity

stimulating stress

Better coping mechanisms neutralise increasing demands

In everyday life, the tightrope walker's balancing act simply equates to the balance of the demands put upon us and the ways in which we deal with them, in other words our coping mechanisms. This is shown in the following illustrations.

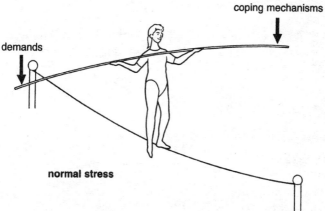

coping mechanisms

demands

normal stress

Demands balanced by coping mechanisms

From time to time, as in the next illustration, the demands made upon us are just too great for us to manage. If we cannot cope with them sufficiently, we experience severe and unpleasant stress.

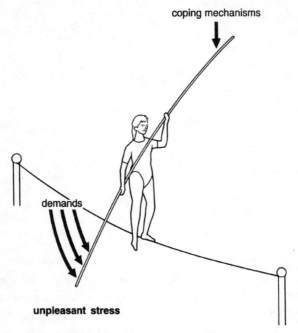

coping mechanisms

demands

unpleasant stress

Demands outweighed by our ability to deal with them

On the other hand, for the self-assured, professional tightrope walker who can confidently skip across the tightrope blindfolded several times a day, there is hardly any challenge left. He no longer needs the pole at all and he craves new and exciting challenges. In his case, there are woefully insufficient demands being made on his admirable and capable coping mechanisms and he feels frustrated, wasted and redundant. Perhaps he has seen other equally skilled tightrope walkers move on to greater things. One of them may now be crossing the wire over Niagara Falls, and another managing it piggyback whilst juggling skittles. When too little is demanded of somebody with more than enough ability to cope, as in the case of someone made redundant or unfairly passed over for promotion, severe stress may be experienced, as illustrated below.

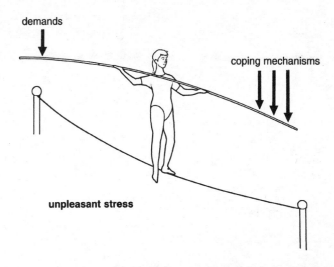

Demands insufficient to challenge our abilities

What the tightrope walker really needs and would relish here is a new challenge: something to break the monotony and boredom, something to stimulate him. A little excitement in his life would do him the world of good. It would allow him to experience the thrill of rewarded achievement, of stimulating stress. Our tightrope walker therefore trains hard for crossing over Niagara Falls. It will be windy, the spray will make the tightrope slippery and thousands of spectators will be watching his every move. But when the going gets tough, the tough get going and when the big day comes he responds to every demand he has made on himself. His coping mechanisms are honed, he has achieved something he has never done before and despite being aware of the stress and the pressure, he feels absolutely wonderful with the elation and euphoria of his success. This is stimulating stress, as shown in the next illustration.

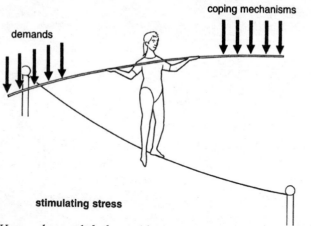

Heavy demands balanced by admirable coping mechanisms

The pace of life for all us tightrope walkers in today's crazy and mixed-up world means that we all experience severe stress at various times. The trick is to keep those occasions to a minimum so that we suffer fewer symptoms of unpleasant stress, and hopefully avoid falling off the tightrope completely into the abyss.

To maintain our stress equilibrium, we have to reduce the number and frequency of demands made upon us, and increase our coping ability to deal with them. We need to experience and enjoy stimulating stress as much as possible by finding the right balance. To do that we have to look at how we experience the pressures from the environment around us, and how we can adjust to them. Learning the techniques and skills required to change the stress balance by adjusting the demands on us, and improving our responses to them, is what effective stress management is all about.

Later sections in the book will describe this more fully, but we first need to understand exactly what happens to us, to our minds, bodies and souls, when we become victims of stress. We need to be absolutely clear about the nature of the physiological stress response, the biology of stress itself.

CHAPTER THREE

WHAT STRESS DOES TO US

Anatomically speaking, all human beings are 'a bundle of nerves'. There are literally billions of interconnecting nerve cells, or neurons, which make up the brain, the spinal cord and all of the peripheral nerve pathways which allow the body to function. Every cell in the human body is influenced in one way or another by the nervous system. It is our information-gathering, storage and control centre, a complex computer operating a highly sophisticated machine. Information is fed into the system through the sense organs and then modified by higher mental functions in the brain. Reaction then takes place according to the instructions transmitted along nerve cells to the rest of the body. Stressful stimuli can have a powerful effect on the function of any part of the nervous system. In its turn, the nervous system acts in a way which is guaranteed to make us respond.

Being aware of the biology of stress and the stress response itself is essential in learning how to recognise the effects of stress on our bodies, and how it influences our performance in everyday situations. It also explains very clearly how stress might affect our health and helps us understand how our own behaviour and personality can create stress by increasing the demands we make on ourselves without similarly improving our coping abilities.

The 'Fight or Flight' Reaction

The nervous system has many functions, some under conscious control and some which are performed automatically. The most basic and primitive function of all, however, is that of survival itself. Many survival responses, like avoiding physical pain, stopping bleeding from wounds and shivering in response to cold, are brought about by the nervous system without any conscious effort of will. At its most acute, the survival response prepares us within milliseconds to meet any life-threatening event head on. This is the famous 'fight or flight' reaction, which has remained primordial and unchanged since time immemorial. It was first described by Walter Cannon of Harvard in the 1930s. Evolution, which has changed so much else, has passed it by without modification. The powerful physical responses it evokes are just as essential and automatic today as they were thousands of years ago, when primitive man fought wild animals with his bare hands, and when fatal injury or death often came unpredictably and swiftly.

In Neanderthal man, the fight or flight reaction prepared him for the ultimate physical challenge. A series of nervous and hormonal reflexes of lightning speed would enable him to either stand and fight the wild animal, or flee the danger as fast as he possibly could. To achieve this, a complex series of biological changes would automatically occur. His heart would beat faster and his blood pressure would rise. His breathing would quicken and his reflexes sharpen. His muscles would fill with blood and his skin would cool and sweat. Extra glucose would pump into his bloodstream and his mental alertness would be heightened, honed and focused. His fighting ability would be enhanced to a degree that would be impossible during any moment of relaxation or unguardedness. Even if he turned to flee his aggressor, the extra oxygen in his lungs, the blood in his muscles and the increased circulation pumping around his body, would enable him to run more swiftly and nimbly than at any other time. The fight or flight reaction is, in short, a life saver, and it is every bit as vital and effective today as it was at the beginning of time.

If an out-of-control juggernaut careers off the road and onto the pavement where pedestrians are walking, they scatter with amazing speed. If an unruly mob of drunken football hooligans rushes towards us waving broken bottles, we escape in the opposite direction pretty damned fast. But if we are cornered like the proverbial wounded beast, we will fight for survival to the last, and all the time the fight or flight reaction is protecting us, defending us and minimising pain to keep us alive. There have even been substantiated reports of people exhibiting superhuman agility and performing Herculean feats of strength when acting under duress. A mother was able to lift a car off a toddler unaided; a man leapt a twelve-foot wall following a bomb explosion; a farm worker walked several miles for help after his arm had been severed by the blades of a combine harvester.

These kinds of life-threatening events do not, thankfully, happen to us every day, although the acute stress response can always be mounted at the drop of a hat. However, minor irritations and frustrations which accumulate in number and which are repeated with tedious regularity, can trigger a different but nevertheless still significant stress response.

The Stress Response

This is less powerful than the fight or flight reaction, but much more insidious. It produces many of the same effects but to a much lesser degree. The person concerned is consequently much less aware of the effects on their emotions and their body and blissfully unaware of the harm that may be done if this continues.

Another major difference in the more run-of-the-mill stress response compared to the fight or flight reaction, is that we never actually get to fight or flee. Most stressors that we come across today are not solved by a punch-up or by running away, so the effects of the stress response have no way of being dissipated. Our modern twentieth-century lifestyle does not permit a purely physical reaction to pressure. Assaulting our boss at work, or sprinting out of a difficult business meeting is not socially appropriate behaviour, however tempting it may be! But our prehistoric, genetically programmed defence mechanisms, which affect every single organ of our bodies, still kick in. They also kick in when we face horrendous traffic queues, when we encounter slow and incompetent ticket clerks at the railway station, or when a rude letter from the bank manager arrives for no justifiable reason. These trivial, but repetitive, annoyances keep us in a constant, unhealthy state of mental and biological arousal, which has no appropriate outlet. Instead, we shout at the children, or slam doors at home to vent our own frustration, but most of the effects of the stress response remain bottled up and repressed.

As we will see later on, this state of affairs is inevitably harmful, but the degree of psychological and physical damage inflicted on any one person will depend very much on their own individual stress threshold.

Your Personal Stress Threshold

Different degrees of pressure and demand are required to produce the stress response in different people. The stress threshold is a highly individual thing. Without challenges, motivation and stimulation, none of us could learn and grow. The stresses in our lives, whatever shape or form they may come in, are only harmful if they are of sufficient intensity and of adequate duration to elicit the stress response. Pressure can sometimes be considerable and prolonged during a fortnight of final exams or in a nail-biting five-setter on the tennis court. But some people have an amazingly well-adapted coping mechanism, which keeps their stress response optimally tuned and will enable them to perform really well – the name of the cool Swedish tennis champion Bjorn Borg springs to mind. Other people might simply wilt under such duress. There are many different factors which determine the triggering of the stress response in any one person, and the illustration below sums them up.

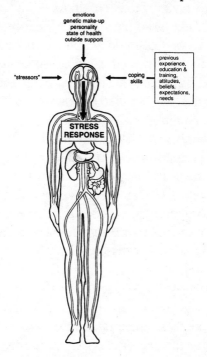

Factors which influence the personal stress threshold

The fact that you are under enormous pressure does not necessarily mean that the stress response will be evoked. What matters is your ability to handle the pressure, because this is what determines the amount of stress you experience. In turn, your ability to deal with the stress depends on many factors. Personality has a lot to do with it. People who set unnecessarily high standards for themselves and who are perfectionist in outlook, are likely to want to cope meticulously with every little problem that comes their way, tidily and without delay. But asking this much of yourself is stressful in itself. Genetically, some people are made this way, whereas others are much more laid-back and have a *laissez faire* attitude to life. Your state of health is important, too. A busy mother with several small children, all under the age of five, who is already tired and then develops pneumonia, or arthritis, will be much less able to handle the increased demands on her than she would otherwise be. If she is isolated and has no social support, things will be even worse.

Emotional factors are also important. There are times when people feel so emotionally threatened by a situation, that the stress response is brought about much sooner, and at a much higher level, than would normally be expected. In these situations anger and aggression could be the outward signs that we have decided to mentally 'fight' and that our body is physically prepared for battle. In a sense, this is a coping mechanism, elicited expressly to deal with the problem. If, on the other hand, the pressures become impossible to contemplate, we become so scared that we mentally 'run away' from whatever is bothering us.

How we interpret the nature of any demand, and how much we perceive it as a threat, depends on our experience of past events, on our upbringing, on our education and training, on our attitudes, and on our beliefs. All of these different factors come into play when we are faced with external pressure. Our brain makes an instant analysis of the nature and degree of any threat and, depending on the result, a certain level of stress response is initiated.

Suppose you are sitting alone at home, on a dark winter's night, and you have just switched off the television, having watched a suspense thriller involving breaking and entering followed by violent assault. You rather regret having watched it in the first place. Now you imagine you are hearing all kinds of unfamiliar noises from outside. Something makes you look up suddenly and you see a grotesque face pressed against the window looking in at you. Your heart leaps, you take an involuntary gasp of breath and clutch your chest. You immediately then jump up and search the room for a weapon. You would really like to run away, but since you are trapped inside the house and the face is outside, there is nowhere for you to go and you may just have to fight.

In this situation, the danger is perceived as being life-threatening so the brain sends out signals to the rest of the body preparing it for the mental and physical crisis that is about to follow. The response is visceral and immediate, and the body is put on physiological red alert. This is a typical example of the full-blown fight or flight reaction. Compare it to the arousal response elicited in a different situation.

You are taking your driving test and you are very nervous anyway. You nudged the kerb reversing around a corner and revved the engine a little too loudly doing the three-point turn. The examiner has given you no clue as to what assessment he is making, but you get the distinct feeling that you have not done very well and that he is deliberately trying to trick you on questions from the Highway Code. Because the test seems to be going on forever, and you are becoming even more nervous as time goes by, you want it to finish as quickly as possible and 'get the hell out'. Your mouth is dry, your hands are shaking a little and your voice is pathetically tremulous. You are close to panic now and starting to lose control, but you know you have to finish the test and answer questions to the best of your ability. Your body is primed to jump out of the car and run away, but that is not an option. Your brain knows this is not a life-threatening situation, but at the same time it is very well aware of the physical symptoms of anxiety you are feeling.

In this case, the stress response is modified and under a greater degree of mental control. You can just about handle it provided it gets no worse. If, on the other hand, the test were to continue for several hours or days, the pressure would become unbearable and something might very well snap unless the tension were to be released. At this level of the stress response the biological adaptive mechanisms are simply overwhelmed and exhaustion follows. This is the stage that everyone should try to avoid as all the harmful and unpleasant aspects of stress stem from it.

Arousal and Relaxation

We all go through life responding to the stresses around us by first becoming mentally 'aroused' to meet the challenges thrown up at us and then 'relaxed' as each crisis passes. Whether we are aroused or relaxed at any one time depends on the nervous system which has two independent branches working in opposition to one another. There is an arousal branch which gears us up to respond to stress (the so-called 'sympathetic' branch) and a relaxation branch which restores our bodies once more to a state of complete rest (the 'parasympathetic' branch).

AUTONOMIC NERVOUS SYSTEM

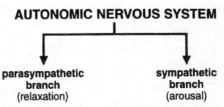

	parasympathetic branch (relaxation)	**sympathetic branch** (arousal)
generally:	promotes rest, digestion, recuperation	prepares body for "fight or flight"
heart:	slows heartbeat	increases heartbeat
blood vessels:	widening in the skin	widening in heart muscle and limb muscle, constriction elsewhere
intestine:	increased activity	decreased activity
pupil of eye:	constricts	widens
brain activity:	relaxation	heightened alertness
lungs:	respiratory passages narrow	respiratory passages widen
sweat glands:	no sweating	sweating
spleen:	at rest	contracts to move stored red cells into circulation
blood coagulation:	normal	increased coagulability
liver and fat cells:	normal	sugar and fat released into circulation
salivary glands:	increased flow of saliva	decreased flow of saliva

The arousal and relaxation branches of the nervous system and their effects on the body

Arousal

The arousal system prepares the body for physical action by bringing about a number of important changes in the body.

- The pulse rate quickens and the heart beats more forcefully.
- Blood is diverted to the muscles of the heart and limbs, and away from the digestive system and the skin where it is of no immediate use.
- Extra red blood cells are pumped into the circulation in order to transport more oxygen around the body from the lungs.
- The respiratory passages widen, increasing the amount of oxygen that can be supplied by the lungs to the rest of the body.
- The skin starts to sweat, allowing for increased heat loss.
- The pupils become wider, allowing more light to reach the back of the eye.
- Blood levels of sugar and fat increase in order to supply more energy to active muscles.
- Mental alertness is enhanced.
- The ability of the blood to clot is increased, protecting against excessive blood loss in the event of any physical injury.

Relaxation

Conversely, the 'relaxation' system is designed to conserve energy, to aid digestion and protect the body from outside influences such as bacterial or viral infection. Increased activity in this division of the nervous system has the opposite effect to that of the sympathetic nervous system.

- The heart rate slows down and the contractions become less forceful.
- The flow of saliva is increased in order to improve digestion.
- The intestine works harder to improve the absorption of food and the elimination of waste products.

- The airways in the lungs become narrower.
- The pupil of the eye constricts, decreasing the amount of light reaching the back of the eye.

These two branches of the nervous system are regulated by means of certain chemicals called neurotransmitters. These chemicals are released at the nerve endings in response to electrical signals from the brain. The sympathetic nervous system is largely controlled by a neurotransmitter called noradrenalin, whereas the parasympathetic nervous system is mainly controlled by a different neurotransmitter, called acetylcholine. This is illustrated overleaf. Most organs in the body will receive neurotransmitter messages from both branches of the nervous system and, since these have opposite effects, the organs will respond in differing ways. So, for example, the sympathetic branch stimulates the heart, but the parasympathetic relaxes it. The digestive system is quietened by the sympathetic branches, whereas the parasympathetic reactivates it, and so on.

The adrenal glands which are situated above each kidney also play a major part in the stress response. They produce three hormones whenever the body is under stress: adrenalin, noradrenalin, and cortisol. Cortisol acts as the body's anti-inflammatory hormone. It fights inflammation and helps to mop up any infection. It assists the other stress hormones to do their job efficiently, and helps to break down the body's fat stores and turn them into a source of energy for the muscles.

The overall stress response is governed very largely by the effects of noradrenalin, adrenalin and cortisol, which bring about all physical changes described above. The instant stress reaction is brought about by the effect of noradrenalin and adrenalin, but this effect only lasts a few seconds. Hormones released into the circulation by the adrenal glands circulate much more slowly to the body organs, so the effect is delayed, but once there, these hormones maintain and prolong the stress response. By having two separate mechanisms whereby it can physically respond to stress, the body is able to sustain the stress response for as long as is necessary to successfully deal with any challenging situation. When the source of stress is abolished, the sympathetic nervous system switches off and the parasympathetic nervous system restores a state of rest and relaxation in the body. The effect of the stress response on the various organs of the body is illustrated opposite.

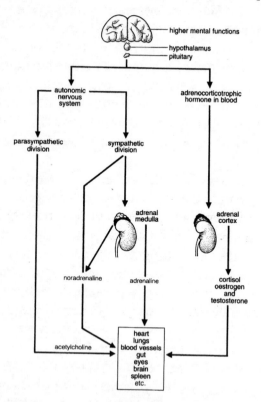

Summary of effects of stress on the body

	Relaxed	Acute stress	Long-standing stress
Heart	Normal heart rate and blood pressure	Faster pulse. Higher blood pressure.	High blood pressure and chest pain.
Intestine	Normal activity	Reduced blood supply. Slow digestion.	Indigestion, heartburn, ulcers, bloating, wind, diarrhoea, irritable bowel syndrome.
Skin	Healthy	Blanched, cool, sweaty.	Dryness, rashes, psoriasis, eczema.
Brain	Calm	Better concentration, enhanced memory, faster reflexes.	Headaches, migraines, tremor, confusion, depression and anxiety.
Mood, emotions	Happy and content	Focused and serious.	Fearful, apprehensive, absent sense of humour. Strained.
Muscles	Normal function	Faster, more powerful contraction.	Muscle tension and strain.
Lungs	Quiet breathing	More oxygen transported to bloodstream.	Asthma, overbreathing, Feelings of suffocation and breathlessness.
Bladder	Functions without conscious thought	Frequent urination.	Frequent urination and conscious discomfort.
Sexual organs	Normal	Impotence in men. Disturbed periods in women.	Impotence, period disturbances. Loss of libido, anorgasmia.

Effects of stress on the organs of the body

How the Brain Controls the Stress Response

The brain carries out the initial stress assessment while constantly processing the information it receives from the sense organs. It puts this information through a kind of sorting process based on previous experience, attitudes and beliefs. Part of the brain also responds to the emotions aroused by any crisis, which may involve rage, apprehension, or even satisfaction, depending entirely on how the person feels about the circumstances in which they find themselves. When the brain has decided what kind of stress response is appropriate it will initiate the production of noradrenalin, adrenalin, and cortisol, and will determine how much is needed of each. This process is illustrated below.

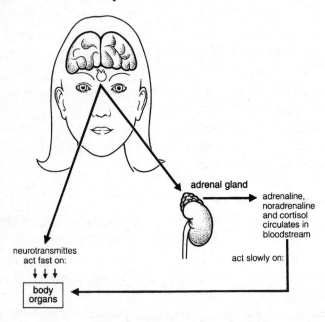

How the brain controls the stress response

Here are three examples of the different ways in which the brain might control your reaction to a stressful situation.

Preparing to Fight

You return home from a pleasant evening out, only to find two masked intruders in the front room of your house. They have ransacked the entire ground floor and have stacked a large number of your valuables in one corner ready to load into their van. They are panicked by your sudden, unexpected arrival and find themselves trapped in an enclosed room. They become aggressive and move towards you with make-shift weapons in their hands. You have no choice but to protect yourself and fight, and so the brain instigates a large release of noradrenalin through the sympathetic nervous system. This enables you to maintain your alertness and to sustain physical effort. Your body is prepared for fighting, and the emotional signs are anger and aggression. You would probably yell or make some other exclamation of rage. Just like more primitive animals, who hiss, bark and bare the teeth when threatened, human beings also make intimidating noises and gestures as warning signals to any attacker, such as clenching the fists and swearing. Mental alertness and body strength are immediately enhanced and you are automatically possessed of an increased level of resolve and power.

Fleeing from Danger

You have returned home from work rather later than usual, on the train, and it is already getting dark. Unusually, you are alone on the station platform as you see the train disappear in the distance. You know there is a long, unlit passageway that you have to walk through in order to reach the car park. You already feel frightened and exposed, but as you start to walk towards the car park you hear a rustling just behind you in the bushes. Your brain tells you that running away as quickly as possible is the correct course of action, and it therefore promotes an immediate rush of adrenalin. This increases your heart rate and boosts your energy supplies to help you run faster. Later, when you reach the safety of your car, and lock the door securely before driving away, you realise with relief how unpleasant that situation was. You felt quite sick, your heart was thumping like crazy, you tensed up and your mouth was dry. It was similar to the unpleasant sensations you remember just before final exams or during a difficult interview. These are the effects of adrenalin. 'If this is what high-powered executives call the thrill of the adrenalin rush, they can keep it!' you say to yourself. In fact, the effects of adrenalin are always unpleasant – it is noradrenalin which gives people a 'buzz'. When it is not being used in the acute stress response, it gears people up mentally and gives them a sensation of euphoria and elation to which they can become addicted.

Coping with the Strain of Long-term Demands

You are busy at work and lead a hectic life at the best of times. Several weeks ago your wife injured her knee, preventing her from walking very far or looking after the children. This coincided with moving house, leaving you tired, worried, and shouldering a great deal of responsibility. These are long-term demands which require a protracted supply of energy and determination. In these situations cortisol and the related sex hormones, oestrogen and testosterone, are secreted by the adrenal glands. Although oestrogen is predominantly the female sex hormone as opposed to the male hormone testosterone, both sexes produce some of each and both hormones play a significant role in our social behaviour and in forming satisfactory relationships. Security, initiative and control of our immediate environment depend to a large extent on our sex hormone levels. When things go against us and appear beyond our control, levels of the sex hormones can fall, leading to poor self-esteem and reduced libido. Conversely, when we feel loved, cared for, satisfied and secure, these hormone levels are elevated. Our self-esteem is increased, we feel better about life generally, and have greater physical energy and sex drive.

The Effect of the Stress Response on our Body

As we have seen, the main effects of the stress response on our body are brought about by the sympathetic nervous system and the adrenal glands, working under the control of the brain. The effects from top to bottom are the following.

- Heightened mental alertness allows thought processes to occur more quickly.
- The pupils dilate to improve vision.
- The skin becomes more sensitive to touch.
- Hearing becomes more acute.
- The sense of smell becomes more sensitive.
- The flow of saliva reduces, leaving the mouth dry.
- The heart beats more quickly and more forcefully, sometimes giving rise to palpitations.
- The circulation of the blood increases, delivering oxygen to all parts of the body.
- The respiratory passageways open up so that the lungs can take in more air, and breathing becomes faster and deeper.
- Stores of glucose and fat in the liver and in the body's fat cells are broken down and mobilised into the blood stream for use as extra energy.
- The digestive system slows down and blood supply to the gut is switched off.

- The spleen releases red blood cells into the bloodstream in order to carry more oxygen around the body.
- White blood cells are released into the blood stream to fight infection or inflammation.
- The kidneys produce less urine in order to preserve the volume of circulating body fluid and to enable the blood pressure to be maintained at a high level.
- The adrenal glands release noradrenalin and adrenalin on a gradual and prolonged basis.
- The blood's ability to clot is increased in order to prevent excessive blood loss from any wounds incurred through trauma or violence.
- The energy supply to the limbs is increased to enable them to function more powerfully and for longer periods.
- Blood flow to the skin is reduced and sweating occurs to reduce the body temperature during sustained muscular activity.

The Effect of Cortisol on our Body

Earlier in this chapter we looked at the effect of cortisol on our body. Under normal circumstances, it is released at a steady rate, but during high levels of stress this rate is vastly increased. From top to toe this gives rise to the following effects.

- Allergic reactions in the body are inhibited, because any breathlessness, red itchy eyes or blocked nose caused by an allergy would seriously interfere with an efficient stress response.
- The efficiency of the immune system is reduced if too much cortisol is produced as a result of prolonged stress, making the body more prone to infection and inflammation, and

possibly to conditions such as arthritis, cancer and ageing as well.

- Blood glucose increases, which may lead to the development of diabetes.
- The various body organs are primed to be more sensitive to the action of noradrenalin and adrenalin.
- Wound healing is promoted by stimulating the cells and enzymes which bring this about.
- The inflammatory response is suppressed and the production of fluid in response to trauma and inflammation can be reduced, for example in the case of injuries to the elbow or the knee.

Emotions and Stress

Emotional factors play a significant part in the stress response. In an experiment, the blood chemistry of two singers playing the lead role in a West End stage musical was analysed. The first sample was taken from the singer making her last appearance in front of a packed auditorium before she relinquished her role to hand over to her understudy the next evening. She was totally in control, having had rave revues all season. She had performed the songs many times before and she felt calm and in control. In fact, she simply basked in the limelight and revelled in the applause. Her noradrenalin levels were high, her adrenalin levels were low, and her cortisol was ticking along at a normal level. Samples taken the following night on the newly appointed understudy revealed a very different picture, however. This was her first night and she was conscious of having a huge mountain to climb in following in the footsteps of her successful predecessor. She had not performed before in front of such an audience and she was aware that she would be judged harshly should she fail. She had not had time to build up much of a rapport with her fellow artistes either, so she felt understandably vulnerable and exposed, and was very much on edge. Her blood sample revealed a high level of adrenalin, an increase in cortisol and only a small increase in noradrenalin.

What Happens when Stress is Prolonged

The first singer's blood sample reflected the blood chemistry of somebody who was prepared for the 'fight' part of the stress response, whereas her understudy's sample reflected the changes involved with fear and 'flight'. Let's suppose the experiment continued and the understudy made a serious mistake on the first night, attracting ridicule from the critics. Her audiences fell and she naturally tended to judge herself harshly as a result. Eventually, this began to play on her mind and she started to feel depressed and fed up. It was a situation she found difficult to escape from – she was even tempted to run away from the stage and never return. This protracted admission of defeat resulted in a large increase in the amount of cortisol circulating in her blood stream, with fairly normal levels of adrenalin and noradrenalin, and probably a small decrease in testosterone. Conversely, the original singer was feeling marvellous. She had enjoyed her West End season and the adulation it brought and whilst revelling in her new-found, blossoming career prospects, she was aware that her understudy had not matched her success. She was elated and felt secure. She had the affection and support of not only her agent, but also of her many colleagues and friends who were proud just to be associated with her. Her testosterone levels increased, giving her a new-found confidence, initiative and drive. The levels of adrenalin and noradrenalin in her blood decreased along with her cortisol, and she was very much in charge and in control of her own destiny.

These examples show how our appraisal of any situation, good or bad, will influence our stress response, and how our emotions affect the chemical messengers circulating in our blood stream.

Mind Over Matter

Fitness instructors and personal trainers will tell us that to perform well we need to apply 'mind over matter'. What they are saying is that we can use our conscious thoughts and emotional reactions to a situation to push our bodies beyond normal limits. The marathon runner who 'hits the wall' at a distance of twenty miles with six still to go, needs to apply mind over matter to succeed. The high jumper who has trained hard to reach the final of his event, but needs to break his personal best to win, has to do the same. The middle-distance runner whose lungs are bursting and whose limbs feel like jelly as he approaches the tape, needs to surpass normal levels of physical limitation by urging his body onwards. All of these athletes can achieve their goals by psyching themselves up for their particular tasks. By deliberately evoking the stress response, by triggering the release of the various neurotransmitters involved, they can produce an impressive and sustained physical effort that would otherwise prove impossible. This ability to break through the pain barrier is once again that primitive reflex that was once solely concerned with ensuring our survival in a hostile environment.

CHAPTER FOUR

HOW WE REACT UNDER PRESSURE

Different people react to life's demands and stresses in different ways. It is neither the demands themselves nor the workload alone which brings about a stress response. Much depends on the ability of the individual to cope with those demands, on their emotional reaction to them, and on their previous experiences.

Personality and temperament are also vital elements. What may be a particularly unpleasant crisis for one person may be interpreted as a thrilling and mind-blowing challenge for another. How we each react to stress, therefore, is highly variable. If we think back to the biology of the stress response and the effect of the various neurotransmitters on the body's organs, it is easy to see what is happening to us physically and mentally when we are under pressure. But the nature of this pressure is the determining factor in whether or not we are stimulated or distressed as a result.

If the demands placed upon us are severe, persistent and unwelcome, and are not matched by our inbuilt capacity to deal with them, we will inevitably suffer from the unpleasant symptoms of stress. If, on the other hand, the pressure is manageable and challenging, we feel nothing but a sense of growing confidence, self-esteem and satisfaction, just like the tightrope walker in Chapter 2. In the following examples, Suzie and Neil are a good illustration of how different people react to similar kinds of pressure, which can appear healthy or unhealthy.

How We React Under Healthy Pressure

Suzie is a twenty-eight-year-old staff nurse working in an NHS casualty unit. She has just been on a well organised and practically based refresher course on resuscitation and life support management. She is on duty one evening when an eleven-year-old boy who has been electrocuted is brought in by ambulance.

Suzie knows exactly what needs to be done and how urgently it is required. She works effectively and efficiently knowing all too well that every minute counts. The outcome is successful and the boy makes a full recovery in due course. The accident and emergency sister and the medical consultant compliment her on her skill and competence. Suzie understandably feels elated. She has experienced enormous job satisfaction and has helped save a young lad's life. She has received the support and praise of her colleagues and feels very much that her career is on the right track. She has experienced all the consequences of a healthy level of stress, and these include feeling stimulated, rewarded, challenged and excited. Elation and euphoria are present too. She feels in control and confident. She also feels capable of rational decision making and clarity of thought, and is well able to cope with what is asked of her.

Automatically, Suzie finds herself smiling, laughing and joking with the people around her. She feels fulfilled and energetic and other people seem attracted to her and charmed by her. She might well be thinking to herself, 'If this is what stress means, then please could I have a lot more of it!'

How We React Under Unhealthy Pressure

Neil, on the other hand, is interpreting his own experiences of pressure quite differently. He is also twenty-eight and works in the same hospital as Suzie. He is a junior casualty officer who only qualified eighteen months previously. He has just started in this department which is all hustle and bustle, a hive of unpredictable and sometimes life-threatening events. A great deal of practical medicine is performed here and he is aware of a discrepancy between his theoretical knowledge acquired at medical school and his ability to work fast and efficiently in this kind of environment. There is also a distinct lack of immediate advice and professional guidance to be had. He is tired anyway, having been up all night, and he is having trouble socially too. He is hardly ever at home and is finding his girlfriend less affectionate and understanding than usual.

When a middle-aged male motorcyclist is brought in by ambulance, unconscious and bleeding, Neil suddenly experiences a feeling of panic. He does not know where to start. He is aware of the ambulance man, the attendant policeman, and other members of staff looking to him to take the initiative, but he feels he just wants to run away. The patient is in danger of expiring in front of him, and the moments are ticking away. As it happens, the eventual outcome in this case is also satisfactory but the treatment is inadequate and slow, and Neil is severely reprimanded by his immediate superior for putting the motorcyclist's life in unnecessary danger. He has experienced all the consequences of an unhealthy and very unpleasant level of stress, and these include a thumping heart, palpitations, butterflies in his stomach, nausea and a dry mouth. He feels rather breathless, and felt the urge to rush off to the loo halfway through his patient's treatment. He is clenching his teeth, biting his nails and shifting from one foot to the other. There is sweat on his upper lip, forehead and palms, although his fingers are cold and clammy to the touch. He feels more tired than ever, and feels hopeless and despairing about the situation. He also feels isolated and depressed. When reprimanded by the senior registrar he feels angry and aggressive, but knows he was at fault because of the unsatisfactory way he dealt with the casualty.

Neil feels frustrated, guilty and worthless. His self-esteem takes a dive and he stops communicating with other members of staff, who equally make little attempt to communicate with him. Later, when the casualty is transferred to the surgical ward for further specialist management, he retreats to the junior doctors' common room, where he drinks and smokes excessively as a means of temporarily blocking out the stress.

How to Recognise Stress

Many of us have experienced the unpleasant side-effects of stress from time to time, some of us more than others. We may recognise signs of continued, excessive stress in ourselves or in other people. People who compulsively perform more than one task at a time ('polyphasing', as it's technically known) are often victims of self-imposed pressure. They always appear rushed and hurried, often failing to finish one job before moving on to the next. They find it hard to concentrate for very long, are unable to make decisions quickly, and forget much of what they have to do. They get their priorities wrong, put things off for another time, and seem unable to get things started. They become accident-prone, and make silly mistakes. They are intolerant of criticism, tending to blame other people rather than themselves. The demands they make on others can be unreasonable, although they themselves are inflexible and find fault in everything and everybody.

These warning signs of excessive stress are well worth recognising, not only in yourself, so that you can take steps to do something about them, but in other people as well, so that you can help and assist them. It will benefit your relationships as well as your working environment, and recognition and awareness of the warning signs of excessive tension form the basis of most stress management courses. There are, of course, signs which cannot be seen but need to be considered, such as rising levels of blood fats and cholesterol and a suppressed immune system. However, not all of these signs and symptoms can be attributed to stress – there may well be other causes. Depression, anxiety and other mental disorders are not always caused by undue stress, although, of course, these conditions are stressful in themselves. Symptoms which mimic stress can also be due to other ailments, such as an over-active thyroid gland, or they can be the side-effects of medications used to treat such conditions.

However, when a pattern of stressful behaviour emerges and many symptoms occur at once without any other obvious explanation, then it is well worth taking a good, critical look at how we are coping with the demands made on us.

CHAPTER FIVE

WHO IS PRONE TO STRESS?

Instinct tells us that personality must be a major factor in the way we respond to stress. Born worriers and those of a 'nervous disposition' are more likely to experience discomfort when put under pressure than those of us who are more laid-back in our approach to life. Some people drive themselves on without a break, whereas others quite naturally choose a gentler and less demanding pace of life. So who is more prone to stress, and why? Are some of us born 'stressed', do we acquire stress or do we have stress thrust upon us? And what are the consequences of all this on our health?

Scientists and pioneers involved in stress research have looked very carefully at the interaction between certain personality types and stress. In the 1930s and '40s the idea of the 'coronary personality' was first put forward to describe a type of behaviour which tended to result in high cholesterol levels in the blood and heart attacks. In the 1950s, two American cardiologists, Mayer Friedman and Ray Rosenman, observed two distinct behaviour patterns in their patients, which they labelled either Type A or Type B.

By observing the patients in their hospital waiting rooms, they noticed the fidgety and impatient restlessness of their cardiac patients, who were characteristically unable to sit still for more than a few minutes and were always anxious to get away to meet self-imposed deadlines. Over eight years, Friedman and Rosenman conducted a research project in over 1500 men and came up with the concept of the 'Type A personality' who, because of exposure to a vigorous and prolonged stress response, seemed more prone to heart and blood pressure problems. Subsequently, Type A behaviour has been universally accepted as a recognised personality trait which the majority of the population exhibit to a greater or lesser degree. It has been estimated that something like eighty percent of our population are mild to moderate Type A personalities with about ten percent exhibiting this behaviour in an extreme form. The remaining ten percent are probably Type B personalities and, although they too can be ambitious and high achievers, the way they achieve their success is quite different to their Type A counterparts. Try the questionnaire at the end of this chapter on page 58 to see how much of a Type A personality you are.

How to Recognise the Type A Personality

Type A people are competitive, ambitious and desperate to achieve. They always appear impatient, hurried and conscious of the time. They constantly seek to exert control over their environment, and are preoccupied with deadlines, intolerant of delay, and generally hostile. Their hostility, however, is generally directed inwards, and they are unable, or unwilling, to express their irritation and anger externally. You rarely see the Type A personality gesticulating wildly and bawling out the opposition. They are more likely to scream silently inside their own heads and take out their frustration by throwing themselves even more vigorously into their work, or through increased physical efforts on the tennis court or in the swimming pool.

Type A personalities also set themselves unrealistic targets and therefore find it difficult to cram all their work into the allotted time. Consequently, they take on more than one project at a time and are often unable to complete one task adequately before moving on to the next. Their irritation and anger often surfaces over very trivial matters and they tend to blow things out of proportion, failing to see the wood for the trees. They pay a lot of attention to detail and are fairly obsessive about numbers, quantities and general accuracy. In conversation they make many references to 'I', 'Me' and 'Myself', but are relatively poor at listening to other people's opinions and viewpoints. They listen with growing impatience to what others are saying, nodding vigorously in an unspoken, non-verbal effort to demonstrate they have already heard all they need.

They also, consciously or unconsciously, see career progression and achievement as being more important than family or friends, listing qualifications and promotions on their curriculum vitae, and completely omitting the fact that they may be married with several children. Unfortunately, they have virtually no insight into their behaviour, appearing blind to their weaknesses and faults. They believe, usually mistakenly, that their way of life must be the most productive. Only a Type A personality could have coined the expression 'if you want something done, ask a busy person to do it'. In fact, the busy person usually volunteers to do it because they are the only fool prepared to do so. The trouble is, they harm themselves in the process, since other tasks and commitments, including social and domestic ones, may be neglected as a consequence.

Whether people are born Type A personalities, or whether they turn into them, is a difficult question. Some personality traits can be inherited to an extent, but attitudes, beliefs and specific behaviour patterns can certainly be modified and altered. For the Type A personality, this can have a hugely beneficial effect on productivity, creativity and health. This type of behaviour develops partly as a result of our upbringing and childhood experiences. Those of us raised in a family with ambitious, career-orientated parents whose values were those of application, self-sacrifice and achievement, often find themselves behaving in the same way. Where love, respect and admiration is conditional upon achievement, the only way we feel we can ever be rewarded and loved, is through driving ourselves ever harder to get to the top. Unfortunately, few Type A personalities ever reach the pinnacle of their ambition and even if they succeed, they soon set themselves another target just as unattainable and just as punishing.

Remember, if you want a stressful life being a Type A personality is certainly a good way of achieving it. Unless, of course, you recognise the dangers and are prepared to do something about them.

How to Recognise the Type B Personality

Type B people are easygoing, calm and controlled. They are generally content with their lot in life, are not easily irritated and appear patient and relaxed. Nor are they easily upset, or provoked into a temper tantrum. They are, however, still competitive and ambitious, or at least they can be. The difference is that, unlike Type A people, they generally do not make themselves ill in the process. The Type B personality faced with a long, stationary queue of traffic will say to themselves 'what the hell', make a telephone call to calmly explain the situation, and enjoy some relaxing music on the car stereo while they have the opportunity. The Type A personality, on the other hand, will rant and rave, frantically seek a way out of the traffic queue, lean on the horn, and curse and swear to themselves.

How to Recognise Stress-inducing Behaviour

Of course, not all of us fit neatly into one or other of these two caricatures. There is generally a bit of both Type A and Type B personalities in most people. There are other types of personality too, which can bring about self-induced stress in a variety of ways. Some people, for example, tend to be naturally passive and shy. They find it difficult to say no, so that others dump more and more work on them when they may be unwilling or unable to take it on. Over a period of time this can result in inner conflict and deep unhappiness. They may even become the victims of somebody else's bullying, and feel they lack control over their own lives. At the opposite end of the scale, they may become bored and unfulfilled because they are reluctant to put themselves forward for promotion or seek a position which exercises their considerable, but chronically underused, skills.

Other people may belong to obsessional personality types, being quite happy in a demanding job, provided it is rigidly controlled and does not involve too much in the way of change. These are conscientious and competent people who thrive on detail, ritual, and tradition. Life is predictable and reassuringly stable, but whenever that security is challenged they experience distress and anxiety.

Then there are the risk seekers in life who like to live 'on the edge'. Conventional, run-of-the-mill jobs do absolutely nothing for them. They thrive on the thrill of taking physical, occupational or financial risks, and appear to be able to live quite happily without stability in their lives. They deliberately cut corners and take shortcuts in order to achieve their ends.

These kinds of people consequently often find themselves in unpleasant and inextricable situations, digging themselves deeper and deeper into self-made holes. They are also likely candidates for nicotine and alcohol dependence, their own self-administered therapy for stress relief.

Many other personality types can be observed. Optimists and pessimists will take the opposing view of certain circumstances to one another, and their resultant stress responses may be markedly different. Another interesting character type is the one that muddles through life using the technique of 'learned helplessness'. By giving up easily, or simply choosing not to be bothered to do the job themselves, they lean on other people to rescue them from certain tasks or commitments. Most of the time this suits their purpose and works quite well, but when the rescuer at any stage complains or opts out of any further assistance, the helpless individual feels resentful, vulnerable and stressed. The 'rescuer' in turn now becomes the persecutor.

American researchers identified a group of people who overreact emotionally to certain situations and then have difficulty settling down again afterwards, so that they remain in a state of high nervous tension most of the time. Their reactions, sometimes referred to as 'neurotic', mean that they have only a limited capacity to deal with demands and stresses without becoming anxious and ill.

Emotional responses to stress are particularly interesting when it comes to our physical well-being. If Type A personalities, with their drive and restlessness, are more prone to heart and circulatory disease, it has also been suggested that people who lack emotional response may be more prone to cancer and other degenerative conditions. Clearly, there is a large degree of overlap in all of these personality characteristics. For example, some Type A people are likely to be anxious, depressed or neurotic and behave the way they do, in order to escape from, or mask, their underlying and unresolved problems.

Finally, there are almost certainly people whose temperament makes them particularly resistant to the harmful effects of stress. The psychologist Shushing Kobos called such people 'hardy personalities'. To them, their life and career are part of an organised life plan which is rational, achievable and fulfilling. They see all change as a challenge and an opportunity. Like the Type A personality, they have a purpose and a goal in life but, in their case, they are able to achieve it without making themselves ill, or driving themselves to unrealistic limits.

Perhaps 'attitude' is the single most important personality factor in determining how vulnerable any individual is to pressure and stress. Attitude can certainly be modified and altered through reappraisal, and by becoming more 'stress aware'. In fact, all of us can work on ways of adjusting our behaviour to moderate our stress response and become more productive at work, happier in our relationships, and more likely to live a long and healthy life. We will be looking at this in more detail in Chapters 13 and 14.

Questionnaire: How Much of a
Type A Personality are You?

For each of the statements below choose the number which most accurately reflects where you stand in terms of your behaviour on a typical day. For example, if you feel rushed and hurried all the time give yourself 10 points in answer to the first statement. If you are never rushed, award yourself 1 point. If you are rushed some of the time, give yourself a number in between.

1	I never feel rushed	1 2 3 4 5 6 7 8 9 10	I'm always rushed
2	I do one thing at a time	1 2 3 4 5 6 7 8 9 10	I'm usually juggling several things at once
3	I do things slowly (talking, eating etc.)	1 2 3 4 5 6 7 8 9 10	I do things at speed
4	I don't mind queuing	1 2 3 4 5 6 7 8 9 10	I hate queuing
5	I'm not pushy or ambitious	1 2 3 4 5 6 7 8 9 10	I'm very ambitious
6	I don't play just to win	1 2 3 4 5 6 7 8 9 10	I'm competitive and want to win
7	I'm laid-back	1 2 3 4 5 6 7 8 9 10	I have to be in control
8	I'm often late for appointments	1 2 3 4 5 6 7 8 9 10	I'm never late
9	I listen to what people have to say	1 2 3 4 5 6 7 8 9 10	I'm irritated by people who don't get to the point quickly
10	I do what is right for *me*	1 2 3 4 5 6 7 8 9 10	It's important to me what others think
11	I find it easy to talk about my feelings	1 2 3 4 5 6 7 8 9 10	I cannot talk easily about my feelings
12	I have lots of interests outside work	1 2 3 4 5 6 7 8 9 10	I'm so busy at work there is little time for anything else

Self-assessment

The higher your score in this questionnaire the more likely it is that you are a Type A personality with behaviour patterns which make you more prone to stress-related heart disease.

Above 85 points
You are 'coronary prone', that is, a prime candidate for a heart attack or a stroke in the future. If you have other risk factors for heart disease – if you smoke, take too little exercise, have a family history of heart attack, and your blood cholesterol is high – you need to make changes now. Delaying matters could kill you.

71–85 points
You tend towards Type A behaviour, but your risk is less than the fully-fledged variety above. You would do well to pay attention to the warning signs of stress in case things begin to get on top of you.

55–70 points
You are fairly relaxed and able to cope with stress although you could still succumb to Type A behaviour if you were not vigilant. You are more of a Type B personality by nature.

Below 55 points
There is very little about you in terms of your behaviour and temperament to make you 'coronary prone'. You are a true Type B and you do not let anyone or anything bother you too much.

CHAPTER SIX

HOW STRESS AFFECTS YOUR PERFORMANCE

Generally speaking, when any of us are faced with a simple challenge, we rise to the occasion and get the job done. As pressure increases, our performance also tends to improve. However, this is only true up to a certain point. When we go over our individual threshold, the unpleasant and unwelcome effects of stress start to influence our efficiency and our behaviour. When taken to the extreme, our performance falls off and deteriorates.

If we remember our tightrope walker from Chapter 2, we can see how this works. On a calm, clear day in good health and supported by a nice taut tightrope and the normal balancing pole, our tightrope walker has no difficulty crossing to the other side. He has done this many times before, and he is quite capable of making the crossing blindfolded, or even on a monocycle. In fact, on the occasions when he achieved this, his stress levels increased but his performance was absolutely brilliant. It was even better than when he made the regular trip.

However, when he attempted to cross the tightrope on a monocycle, blindfolded, and with his brother on his shoulders, it proved just a little too much. He had never attempted it before, he was nervous about whether he would actually be able to do it, and because his centre of gravity was higher than it would be with him making the trip alone, his balance was not nearly as good. The balancing pole was not heavy enough to restore equilibrium when he faltered, and so the tightrope walker subsequently lost all of his customary control and co-ordination. As a result, his performance was awful. He progressed only a few metres along the rope before awkwardly falling off into the safety net. Spectators who had not watched before were totally unimpressed, and saw none of the undoubted talent that the tightrope walker possessed. Some even asked for their money back.

In this case, too many demands and too many stresses reduced the tightrope walker's efficiency and performance dramatically. This is what happens to any of us when we surpass our individual stress thresholds, as Sandra's experience showed.

When Stress Becomes Overwhelming

Sandra was twenty-nine and married to Ray, a pilot in the Royal Air Force. They had two children aged seven and three, when a happy 'accident' occurred leaving Sandra expecting again. Being a well-organised, family-orientated and happy-go-lucky couple, neither she nor Ray had any doubts they would be able to support a third child in the family, even though they realised it would be a strain. Ray's long absences on duty abroad and the poor, cramped accommodation in which they lived was a problem but even on their low income, and despite Sandra's relatively isolated existence, they felt they could manage. What they did not reckon on, however, was twins. Whilst Ray was halfway around the world complications during the confinement arose and the babies were born prematurely in their father's absence. The strain of looking after the older children, whilst spending as many hours as she could visiting the sick twins in the local hospital, left Sandra drained and exhausted. When the twins eventually came home she was overwhelmed. Life became a constant round of feeding, cleaning, washing, dressing and carrying. She felt guilty that she could not cope.

Ray was shocked to see Sandra in such a state when he returned. She could not sleep and had lost weight. She saw no humour in anything, was unable to show Ray any affection, and could see no light at the end of the tunnel. Ray simply could not understand. What had happened to his bubbly, capable, ever-loving girl? Why was she suddenly unable to cope, making mistakes and giving him the cold shoulder? Any attempt he made to help was derided and scorned. He simply did not have the experience to recognise that Sandra had developed postnatal depression as a result of the stresses she had been under and the circumstances in which she found herself.

Sandra had certainly exceeded her personal stress threshold some weeks before. Had she been able to reduce the demands and responsibilities forced upon her at that time, things might have been very different. But stresses which affect families are not always easy to handle, especially for a busy housewife who often has little support and encouragement in the course of her long working day.

Fortunately, Sandra's postnatal depression was successfully treated whilst her children were temporarily looked after at home by relatives and friends. Ray was able to take some compassionate leave, and the GP and health visitor were meticulous in supervising Sandra's gradual but nevertheless full recovery.

Good Stress, Bad Stress

The balance between the positive and negative effects of stress on performance and efficiency were first described in 1908 by Yerkes and Dodson at the Harvard Physiology Laboratory. They showed that when pressure increases, so does efficiency and performance. But they also demonstrated that this relationship is valid only to a certain degree. When stress and pressure continue to increase, the anxiety which results produces a reduction in performance and efficiency. This is illustrated below.

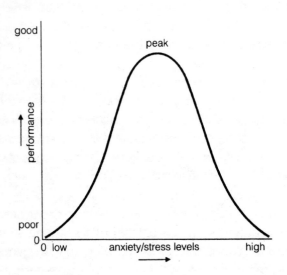

A simplified version of the Yerkes-Dodson curve

It is easy to see from this simplified graph that there is a certain point where maximum performance can be achieved at the pinnacle of the upward slope of the performance curve.

Here, there is optimum stimulation and challenge and we are achieving our best ever work. Yes, there is a degree of stress present, but because we are handling it well, we still feel rewarded, satisfied and effective. In this situation, we are mentally attuned to making decisions, and we are also more creative and aware.

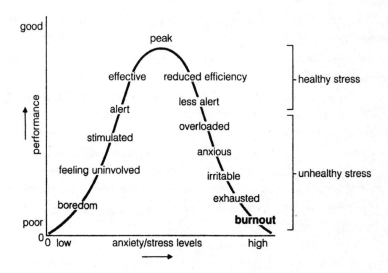

The Yerkes-Dodson curve showing how performance, stress and our emotions are interrelated

We also feel confident and in control of the circumstances in which we find ourselves. This level of stress, therefore, is good and fulfilling stress. It is also healthy stress because it is associated with a level of adrenalin which makes us feel great but which does us no long-term damage, and with fairly low levels of both adrenalin and cortisol. It would be easy to imagine that when faced with less challenging demands we would experience no stress at all and no symptoms. But ironically, the opposite is true. When our coping abilities outweigh the challenges that life puts before us, we feel frustrated and bored. In a work situation, we feel undervalued and unappreciated, and this can be very stressful in itself. So, either too little or too much stress can be associated with a range of unpleasant and stressful emotions, as illustrated in the graph on the previous page.

With no demands made upon us at all, we feel isolated, left out and bored. As we are given more to do and fresh challenges to face, we become more involved and stimulated. Our enthusiasm is triggered, and we become more alert and aware. Given yet more responsibility, we soon find ourselves making decisions and taking the initiative. Our creativity improves to match our efficiency, and soon we reach the pinnacle of the curve. Now for the first time we feel euphoric and fulfilled. Up to now, it has been hard-going and tedious. We have felt many of the unpleasant effects of stress and some of them, if ignored, would eventually have damaging effects on our health.

Right now, though, having reached our optimal levels of performance and stimulation, the increased action of noradrenalin has improved our concentration, our learning and decision making abilities. We feel alert, mentally able and totally aware. Regrettably, we cannot stay in this position all the time.

People in this situation are often perceived by others as being so competent and efficient that they should be quite capable of taking on more. Some individuals, particularly Type A personalities, relish the thought. For them it means attaining a level of achievement worthy almost of heroism. But almost before they know it, they find themselves snowed under. They have taken on so much that they are unable to finish each task in the allotted time, and they start to worry. They start trying to perform more than one job at a time, never finishing anything very effectively. There is no time left to be creative, or to reflect on why things are going wrong. There always seems to be more work coming in than going out, they have less time to listen to other people, and have difficulty concentrating on the job in hand.

By now, they are on the slippery slope to total burnout. They find it harder to make swift, important and correct decisions. They become irritable and frustrated, blaming other people and becoming cross over trivial difficulties. Anxiety mounts and they feel constantly tired and worn out. At this position in the performance curve, they are so totally exhausted that they are of little use to man or beast. Furthermore, they are acutely aware of how awful they feel, both mentally and physically. Their work colleagues and family become concerned at how drawn and haggard they look. They may also be relying far too heavily on alcohol, cigarettes or other escapist behaviour to cope with their hugely stressful situation.

The effect of stress on performance is not only of huge significance for the individual, but also to commerce and industry. The enormous financial costs resulting from absenteeism due to stress-related disorders and loss of qualified personnel through premature retirement or ill health are enormous. Even without these more obvious consequences, a demoralised, underperforming and inefficient workforce will ultimately be reflected in a nose-diving balance sheet and depressed commercial turnover. It therefore makes good sense not only for individuals but also for companies and organisations to appreciate the importance of setting up the right environment and atmosphere in which their employees can work.

You can apply the Yerkes-Dodson law to every aspect of your life. If you can recognise just where you are on the curve at any one time, and in each compartment of your life, you can then take steps to move towards a happier, more fulfilling and optimally stressful position on the performance curve.

CHAPTER SEVEN

WHAT MAKES US STRESSED

Life itself is stressful from the moment we are born to the moment we take our last breath. At a basic biological level, we are programmed to do everything we can to maintain the status quo in terms of our environment. Technically known as *homeostasis*, it simply means preserving a certain stability about everything that happens to us. Anything that challenges that stability at whatever level is therefore perceived as a threat. If our various adaptive mechanisms are able to cope with these challenges, stability is preserved.

If, on the other hand, the threat continues and our coping mechanisms are overwhelmed, then stress occurs and we suffer the consequences. Everything depends, of course, on the way we perceive each threat, and our personal attitudes and beliefs. Some people imagine certain circumstances to be threatening when in reality no threat is present. Others will hardly bat an eyelid in times of crisis.

Almost anything which forces us to adjust to change is potentially stressful and most stress arises these days when our self-esteem and status are questioned. These doubts threaten the stability and security of our careers and our positions in society. Very occasionally we may be confronted with threats to our actual physical survival, but thankfully these situations are few and far between.

The Most Common Sources of Stress

There are many sources of pressure in our lives, some of which are good for us. They stimulate, and motivate us to perform better. Any increased level of stress is all very well if our coping abilities are sufficient to deal with it. If, however, the various demands and pressures which we experience are intense and prolonged, then, no matter how well equipped we are to cope with them, we will eventually crack. Psychologists have, over the years, tried to draw up league tables of stress values for all the various changes and transitions that any individual might have to confront in their lifetime. Probably the best known of these is the Holmes and Rahe Social Readjustment Rating Scale which is illustrated opposite. This scale is designed to predict the likelihood of any future stress-related illness.

By breaking down sources of stress into family, personal, work and financial areas this scale can give a rough indication of the stress an individual is under at any one time. Originally, the researchers questioned several hundred people about the circumstances in their lives which necessitated the most 'social readjustment'. Forty-three sets of circumstances were mentioned as being the most frequently stressful, and what was particularly interesting was that although some of the events were unpredictable, or even traumatic, some were situations normally associated with pleasure and enjoyment. Everybody would consider bereavement and illness as stressful, for example, but even the change required in facing up to marriage, pregnancy, moving house or changing jobs engenders a certain degree of stress.

The arbitrary value of 100 life-change units was given to the death of a partner, and all the other sources of stress were

LIFE EVENTS: check your score and assess your risk

Death of partner	100
Divorce	73
Separation from partner	65
Jail sentence	63
Death of close family member	63
Injury or illness to yourself	53
Marriage – your own	50
Given the sack at work	47
Reconciliation with partner	45
Retirement	45
Ill health in member of family	44
Pregnancy – your own	40
Sexual problems/difficulties	39
Addition of new family member	39
Major business or work changes	39
Change in your financial state	38
Death of friend	37
Change to a different type of work	36
More arguments with partner	35
Take on a large mortgage	31
Mortgage or loan foreclosed	30
Change in responsibilities at work	29
Child leaves home	29
Trouble with in-laws	29
Outstanding personal achievement	28
Wife begins or stops work	26
Child begins or ends school	26
Change in living conditions	25
Change of personal habits	24
Trouble with boss or employer	23
Change in working hours or conditions	20
Change in residence	20
Child changes schools	20
Change in church activities	19
Change in social activities	18
Change in sleeping habits	16
Change in number of family get-togethers	15
Change in eating habits	15
Holiday	13
Christmas (coming soon)	12
Minor violations of the law	11

Holmes and Rahe Social Readjustment Rating Scale

measured in relation to this. Interestingly, any major change in your financial status, for example getting into debt, or becoming bankrupt, ranked as being even more stressful than the death of somebody very close. This may seem bizarre at first, but it is because of the enormous lifestyle changes a ' ɔ decrease in earnings brings about. It was also shown that an equivalent amount of stress was experienced by people getting married as by people faced with serious ill health.

Keeping a Check on Your Life Event Score

In order to assess the amount of accumulated stress people were under, researchers asked people to add up the number of life-change units they had run up in the last year. For most of us, there is a ten percent risk that we will suffer a serious threat to our health during the course of the next twelve months. But using the Holmes and Rahe scale our accumulated life event score during the previous year can be used to indicate our projected risk of illness in the future. It is estimated that any score over 150 is associated with a fifty percent chance of a major health breakdown, and a score of 300 or more with an eighty percent chance during the following two years. It is only those of us (the lucky few) who have a score of less than 100 who are considered to have no increased health risk.

This is a fairly neat method of measuring our individual levels, but it has its limitations because each and every one of us reacts differently to these major life events, depending on our personalities and attitudes. But it is still wise to try to identify the various causes of stress in our everyday lives, and to consider how well we cope with them.

A specially modified version of the Holmes and Rahe rating scale provides you not only with another method of working out just how tough life has been on you in the last year, but, more importantly, a means whereby you can ponder how much these life events have affected you. The following is a list of the ten most stressful life events in order of importance, followed by their stress score.

- Death of a Partner (10)
- Imprisonment (9)
- Divorce (8)
- Marriage (7)
- Marital Separation (6)
- Pregnancy (5)
- Marital Reconciliation (4)
- Serious Personal Injury or Illness (3)
- Getting the Sack or redundancy (2)
- Retirement (1)

A score of more than twenty points accumulated over the last year means that life has been pretty hard on you recently, but it does not necessarily mean that you have not been able to handle it. A lot depends on your temperament and ability to cope. If you want to find out to what extent you have been affected by the problems in your life of late, then try completing the short questionnaire which concludes this chapter, and apply it to each of the life events you have recently experienced.

Since the most important aspects of our lives revolve around our relationships with our family, friends and work, it is hardly surprising that most of the hardship that people experience in their lives arises from these areas. Look how many of them are reflected in the life events list of stressful situations. Problems in marriage, difficulties with the children, arguments with the neighbours and confrontations with the boss or other colleagues in the workplace are all in the table.

Another major source of stress common to many of these events is uncertainty. For many of us, worrying about what *might* happen is actually much worse than what ultimately *does* happen. In other words, it is the unpredictability of the stress that causes the problem. Not having a time limit on a particular problem, or having to leave a decision totally in the hands of somebody else and out of our own control, is particularly difficult for most of us to accept.

In some studies, for example, fear of redundancy was much greater than the redundancy itself when it finally took place. Having said that, the people who worried most were the best prepared when the bombshell finally happened, as they had already made contingency plans for the future. They had been 'stressed' but had handled it in an appropriate and useful way, whereas the people who had gaily carried on as if nothing was happening suffered greater emotional trauma when redundancy actually occurred. However, we will look at stress in the workplace in more detail in Chapter 9.

Questionnaire: How Well Do You Handle Stress?

	Never	Hardly Ever	Sometimes	Often
My mind kept returning to the problem				
I did not let myself become upset when I thought about it				
I tried to blank it from my mind				
It stopped me sleeping or kept waking me up because I worried about it				

Self-assessment

Going back now to the number of stress points you had for the life events, adjust them in the following way. For every time you answer 'Never', give yourself a score of 0, for every 'Hardly Ever' give yourself 1, for every 'Sometimes' give yourself 2, and for every 'Often' give yourself 3.

If your score is more than 6 for any of the life events you have suffered in the last year, then you should double your score of stress points for that particular event. For example, you may have you scored 4 stress points for marital reconciliation following a painful separation the same year. If you were often preoccupied with worries about this during the day, tried to ignore it, and then found you were disturbed by unresolved anxieties at night, your score would double to 8.

If you later divorced, despite the earlier reconciliation, you would have a further 8 stress points from the life event scale, doubling to 16 if the impact it had on you was severe. This would now put you on a total score in the last year of 24 – a significantly high level bearing in mind that anything over 20 signifies an exaggerated degree of stress.

CHAPTER EIGHT

WHAT ARE THE SYMPTOMS OF STRESS?

All symptoms and illnesses are influenced by our emotions and our mental state to a certain extent. Something like three-quarters of all consultations carried out with family doctors in this country are stress related in some form or another. People are anxious, for example, or suffer from the physical symptoms of palpitations, loss of appetite, and irritable bowel syndrome. Others may be depressed, will feel unduly fatigued, have frequent headaches, and loss of sex drive. Take a look at the illustration on the following page to see the effects of stress on health.

Physical symptoms can, in turn make both anxiety and depression worse. Physical ailments which are caused or aggravated by psychological factors are known as 'psychosomatic' disorders, and every GP's surgery is full of them. Often they are merely the early warning signs that an individual is being pressurised beyond their stress threshold, and their body is telling them to slow down. As the saying goes, death itself is the ultimate way in which the body tells us to slow down. But by then, of course, it is too late.

Much has been made in recent years of the importance of excessive stress in creating ill health. But even with all the scientific research at our disposal over the last two or three decades, there is no doubt that the link between the two has been greatly unappreciated. The costs to the individual and

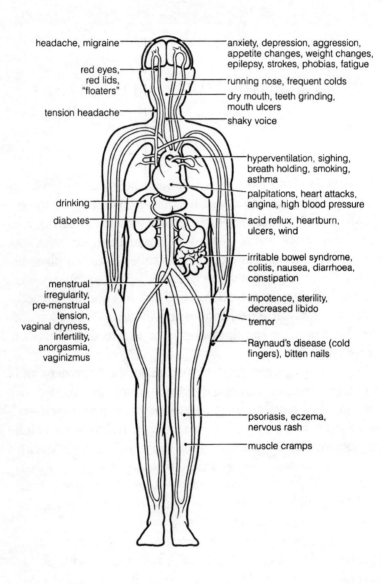

The effects of stress on health

the family are enormous in all sorts of ways. Anyone who brings the pressures of their work home with them will not be able to love and care for their family as they would otherwise be able to do, and relationships can seriously suffer. If they turn to drink, or smoke excessively, this may lead to anti-social and unacceptable behaviour with far-reaching physical consequences.

People under stress are also more accident-prone, and the cost to commerce and industry of stress-related disorders is huge. Over 100 million working days are lost in Britain as a result of stress, with absenteeism costing the country over three billion pounds every year. Organisations suffer because highly qualified and experienced staff resign as the only way to escape from unhealthy levels of stress. Premature retirement and disability also take their toll. The cost of treatment to the National Health Service is crippling, matched only by the financial expense of sick leave to industry as a whole.

The Most Common Symptoms of Stress

A range of stress-related symptoms forms a pattern of warning signs which, if we neglect or ignore them, may make us more prone to serious long-term diseases. The following lists show the most common behavioural and physical symptoms which are likely to be associated with excessive levels of stress in daily life.

Behavioural Symptoms
- Over-eating and obesity
- Loss of appetite and anorexia
- Increased cigarette smoking
- Increased alcohol intake
- Increased caffeine consumption

- Increased or first-time substance misuse
- Constant irritability with other people
- Difficulty in making decisions
- Suppressed anger
- Difficulty concentrating
- Loss of sense of humour
- Paranoia
- Feeling out of control
- Feeling unable to cope
- Inability to finish one job before starting on another
- Feeling like crying at the least little thing
- Lack of interest in hobbies after work
- Constant tiredness and exhaustion
- Feeling tired, even after a night's sleep
- Decreased sex drive

Physical Symptoms

Heart and circulation
- Chest pain
- Palpitations
- Migraine
- Headaches

Digestive system
- Indigestion
- Nausea
- Heartburn
- Loss of appetite
- Diarrhoea
- Constipation
- Flatulence
- Stomach cramps

Nervous system
- Tremor and shaking
- Fainting episodes
- Nervous ticks and twitches
- Foot tapping
- Nail biting
- General jumpiness
- Insomnia and other sleep disorders

Muscles and joints
- Tension headaches
- Muscle cramps and spasms
- Neck pain
- Back pain
- Rheumatoid arthritis

The skin
- Onset or worsening of eczema
- Onset or worsening of psoriasis
- Increased sweating at normal temperature
- Worsening of baldness
- Cold fingers and toes

Sexual disorders
- Reduced libido
- Infertility
- Menstrual irregularity
- Failure to reach orgasm
- Premature ejaculation
- Impotence

General
- Loss of weight

- Frequent urination
- Worsening of asthma
- Frequent colds and 'flu
- Tuberculosis and other infections
- Itching

All of these symptoms, both behavioural and physical, ultimately occur because of the inappropriateness of our primitive fight or flight stress response, and the fact that it has no physical outlet these days. Although our lives are not threatened as our ancestors' frequently used to be, our self-esteem and security at home and at work are often made vulnerable. The stress response, however, always functions in the same way, triggered by a surge in activity of the sympathetic nervous system and the release of stress-related hormones.

The physical changes which are brought about prepare us for fight or flight, but in most situations this is of little use to us. Taking a crowbar to a parking meter which has taken our money without registering time on the clock solves nothing. Thumping the boss, or roaring off up the road to chase a dangerous or aggressive driver is pointless. The less aggressive flight reaction is hardly appropriate either. The ferry captain who abandons the bridge as he approaches harbour in bad weather, or the product manager who runs out of the sales conference in mid-speech, do nobody, especially themselves, any favours.

Our ancient life-preserving defence mechanisms certainly enhance our level of 'nervous arousal' but the problem in today's society is that most overstressed people have an inability to reduce it again. The branch of the nervous system which is designed to bring about a state of relaxation and tranquillity becomes decreasingly effective, with the end result that the stressed individual is permanently in a state of 'red alert'. It is this undiluted and relentless bombardment of stress-related hormones and chemicals which weakens the body.

Stress-induced Conditions

All of the following medical conditions are now well recognised as being induced by stress.

- Hypertension (high blood pressure)
- Heart attack and angina
- Strokes
- Migraine
- Peptic ulcers
- Irritable bowel syndrome
- Ulcerative colitis
- Gastritis (inflammation of the stomach)
- Pruritus (intense itching)
- Asthma
- Hay-fever and allergies
- Menstrual irregularities
- Rheumatoid arthritis
- Hyperthyroidism (overactive thyroid gland)
- Diabetes mellitus
- Eczema and psoriasis
- Tuberculosis and other infections
- Depression
- Anxiety
- Obesity
- Anorexia nervosa
- Insomnia
- Sexual problems

The nervous system controls the function of almost all of our body organs, and alters their response in times of stress. In Chapter 3 we looked at what stress does to the body, and how prolonged stress can cause chronic ailments. Stress clearly has a significant contributory influence on a wide range of medical disorders, but how exactly is the physical damage created? How can the development of certain cancers be attributed to the detrimental effects of stress? Why does coronary heart disease, which results in angina and heart attacks, affect so many Type A people, who are often the most vulnerable to tension? Are women who have had breast cancer in the past more prone to recurrence if they are currently experiencing a stressful life event, as some researchers have suggested? Can we prevent the threat of heart attack or stroke at a fairly young age by adjusting our lifestyle and reducing the pressures on us now?

The answer is yes. We are all able to modify and alter our behaviour and lifestyles in such a way as to reduce our risks of illness. Individuals and their families can certainly benefit from making such changes, and enlightened employers would do well to take on board the importance of a less stressful workplace, enabling their personnel to stay happy and healthy.

Everyone should know a little about how common stress-related diseases develop, if only so that they can be aware of the warning signs. We have already looked at the general effects of the stress response on the body. If we consider some of the more serious stress-related illnesses in turn, we can see how a chronically exaggerated stress response wreaks such havoc.

Heart Attack
A heart attack is caused when part of the heart muscle responsible for pumping blood around the body is totally

starved of blood supply and oxygen. Partial reduction in supply results in pain, or angina, just as we might suffer from pain in a leg muscle during vigorous physical activity. The reason why there is an interruption of blood flow to the heart muscle depends on several factors, all of them influenced by stress.

The main reason is that cholesterol and other fatty deposits build up on the inside lining of the coronary arteries which supply the heart muscle with blood. Wherever this happens narrowing occurs, reducing blood flow and oxygen supply. Stress raises the levels of cholesterol and fats, circulating in the blood, resulting in hardening of the arteries. As the cholesterol deposits accumulate, increased restriction of blood flow will occur.

Stress works in other detrimental ways too. Noradrenalin narrows the blood vessels by making them contract and also makes the blood 'stickier' and more likely to clot. When these two reactions take place in the coronary arteries which feed the heart muscle itself, the result can be life threatening. There is additional evidence that circulating noradrenalin and adrenalin may have a direct effect on the heart muscle cells, leading to abnormal electrical signals and abnormal heart rhythms.

High Blood Pressure
In the vast majority of cases high blood pressure (hypertension) is a silent disease. There are hardly ever any symptoms and the blood pressure gradually creeps up over the course of many years. Doctors check the blood pressure level from time to time to monitor whether any increase has taken place. High blood pressure is associated with strokes and heart disease, so it is a major factor in the two commonest causes of death in the Western world.

Nobody knows exactly why most people develop high blood pressure but it is generally believed that high levels of stress hormones cause the blood vessels to constrict, leading to a rise in blood pressure which over the years becomes self-perpetuating. When the blood pressure rises, the heart has to work harder and its oxygen demands increase. The heart muscle, just like any other, enlarges when made to work more vigorously and eventually, if the blood pressure remains high, the blood vessels thicken and become less elastic. When this happens they are no longer able to relax and widen to reduce blood pressure again. So the blood pressure remains permanently high, and will continue to increase as the years go by and as stress increases.

Raised Cholesterol

An elevated level of cholesterol in the blood is a major risk factor for heart disease and strokes. Along with glucose and other fatty substances, cholesterol is mobilised from the liver and fat cells whenever the stress response demands it, although a small proportion of cholesterol in our bodies comes from our diet. Ideally, it is used for the additional energy demands of active muscles drummed into action by the fight or flight reaction. Since this hardly ever happens in modern life, the cholesterol is never fully utilised. Instead, it is laid down on the inner lining of blood vessels, including those of the carotid arteries which supply the brain and the coronary arteries which supply the heart.

Factors other than stress also contribute to raised cholesterol levels, notably smoking and a diet rich in saturated fats. The genetic influence is strong too, and although we cannot change who our parents were, we can certainly do something about our diet and smoking habits. We can also do something about stress.

The Immune System

It has long been thought that severe and persistent stress can reduce our resistance to simple colds and coughs. People under pressure are forever complaining that they suffer from one cold after another or are just simply 'run down' and fed up.

Recent research has gone further than this and suggested that much more serious conditions, such as rheumatoid arthritis, diabetes, allergy, asthma and even cancer may develop partially as a direct result of undue stress. It is also known, for example, that a patient's emotional reaction to the diagnosis of cancer seems to affect the outcome. People who fight the condition, and who are determined to win through, seem to fare much better than those who turn their faces to the wall and away from life. 'Giving up' in this way seems to reduce our coping mechanisms so much that we passively allow cancer cells to act more aggressively.

On the other hand, too much battling against life's accumulated problems may increase the level of cortisol excessively, an effect known to suppress the activity of our immune systems. We know, for example, that too much cortisol when taken in the form of steroid medication makes us more prone to infection. We know that it makes us put on weight and breaks down protein in our bodies. It affects our white blood cells and reduces the level of circulating antibodies.

Whatever age we are, we all have large numbers of potential cancer cells circulating in our bodies. Our immune system must be capable of mopping them up and eradicating them since only a few of us ever develop cancer. If the immune system can be damaged by the effects of cortisol, which is one of the main components of the stress response, then stress can make the development and progress of cancer more likely. This is one of the possible reasons why women with breast cancer can become more prone to recurrences when experiencing stressful life events.

Recognising the Warning Signs in Other People

It is important to ask yourself how you feel and whether stress is getting to you. Take time to sit down and take stock of significant life events in the last year of your life, and assess your accumulated number of life-change units to see how vulnerable you may be to ill health in the future. You can also look at how you have coped and adjusted to these situations and circumstances. But it is also useful to look at the early warning signs of tension and discomfort in the people around you. It is an advantage to be aware of the symptoms of stress which may be present in your partner, in other family members, in friends or in colleagues at work. This is especially important if you are in any kind of position where you are responsible for the health and safety of others in the workplace.

You do not have to be a genius to spot these warning signs but the following list, although not exhaustive, includes most of the common early symptoms.

- Reduced performance and efficiency
- Increased absenteeism
- Smoking and drinking more
- Constant irritability
- Suppressed anger
- Rapid, unpredictable mood swings
- Indecision
- Constant fatigue

- Anxiety and/or depression
- Hypochondria
- Loss of sense of humour
- Inability to complete each task fully
- Paranoia
- Lack of interest in hobbies
- Extreme pessimism or optimism
- Below standard personal appearance

If employers or work colleagues are able to recognise any of the above signs, they can be instrumental in making the changes which will reduce the damage caused by extreme stress. In turn, they may be rewarded by better productivity and performance, and a lower rate of absenteeism.

If a partner or another member of the family is affected, then the benefits of stepping in to help are even greater. Merely talking things through may be the first step towards recovery. Any problem shared is a problem halved, as they say, but it also means that two minds can concentrate on any necessary remedial action. Team work of this kind is merely part and parcel of the respect and support which all of us need to succeed. The psychological anguish and the physical discomfort prevented can not only cement stable and happy relationships, but also offset the ravages of both short- and long-term disease.

CHAPTER NINE

STRESS AND YOUR JOB

Why Do We Work?

Until relatively recently, work for most people was something they considered a necessary evil in order to survive. Employment was a means to an end, a way of providing the basic necessities to eke out a living for themselves and for their families. As conditions of work improved, however, and as a welfare state developed, employment for some, especially those with skills and higher qualifications, came to be regarded as more of a privilege than as a means of survival, and the psychological benefits became clear. These days, increasing job satisfaction gives people a purpose and a meaning in life without which they would feel less valued and appreciated. The majority of people would still choose to work even if they could afford not to, and this is borne out by the numerous National Lottery winners who voluntarily carry on in their jobs despite having no need of the money.

The alternative, unemployment, has been shown to be stressful in itself, but this is not to say that we should all be grateful for having a particular job, nor that we are all suited to the job in which we find ourselves.

Hassles at Work

For many people the work they do is one of the greatest causes of stress and unhappiness in their lives. Some feel forced to work because the bills simply cannot be paid without it, and others tolerate it as a means of escape from domestic strains or pressures elsewhere. Animosity towards our bosses or colleagues is common and working conditions, even in this day and age, leave much to be desired. Even those of us who are 'married' to our work may have become so bogged down with the routine and bureaucracy of it all that we have just lost sight of why we chose to do the job in the first place. And then there are the countless thousands who, having earned their right over several decades to a fulfilling retirement by subjugating the interests of their family, leisure pursuits and social life, suddenly find that the absence of work leaves a vacuum which is hard to fill.

Working to Keep a Home Together

There are also the millions of housewives, househusbands and carers who may not be paid at all but whose job it is to cook, clean, shop, support the breadwinning partner, raise and educate the children, control the everyday running of the household, and generally juggle a myriad number of essential chores. They too are subject to stress in their job, and in many ways may be even more exposed to it than most because they often work in isolation and have no one to encourage them or to whom they can delegate tasks during the course of their extended working days. No office parties, Christmas bonuses or business lunches for them either!

An Increasing Problem

For all these people I have deliberately written this extended chapter on job stress since I recognise it as being increasingly significant as we near the new millennium. Traditionally, it was always thought that people who had problems at home would not perform well at work and indeed it was, and still is, true. But equally, people whose jobs are not going well take their problems home with them. Because they avoid talking about those problems, the stresses are not communicated and all the family see is the morose, grumpy, ill-tempered individual whom they once used to recognise as 'daddy' or 'mummy'. Individuals who can readily separate their homelife from their working careers are truly few and far between, and I believe that hassles at work are now a major source of serious emotional and social problems for families as a whole. This chapter is therefore dedicated to addressing these particular issues.

Change

Dramatic and rapid changes have occurred in the modern workplace. Not so long ago, we were all being confidently assured that with the advent of new technology, we could all look forward to a shorter working week with an increasing amount of leisure time, and the opportunity to see more of our families. In fact, the opposite has occurred. The boom in information technology, with the availability of faxes, personal computers, mobile telephones, and electronic mail has, if anything, increased the pressure at work. It has created a faster pace of working, and the need to take on board new skills, new working practices, and new technologies. Change is always stressful, particularly when it is forced upon us. Many people, in many different jobs and occupations, find themselves struggling to keep pace with the brave new world.

Dual Careers

Another recent trend resulting from the increasing number of women working full time is the dual career family. There are obvious advantages in the amount of disposable income and the rewards and satisfactions of both partners enjoying a career. It solves the problem of the unfulfilled woman, who resented being the 'little woman at home', and it relieves the strain on the man, who no longer has to be the sole breadwinner. However, dual career families create different problems.

Anyone under stress at work (and most of us are) should naturally expect support, understanding and love from their private relationships and home life. When this last refuge from the tension of work disappears, the partner we looked to for these things can easily become a competitor, and home life can become a battle ground. Domestic jobs are no longer done during the week by the partner not in paid employment so the weekends become the time for the mundane and routine tasks involved in keeping the household going. Leisure time is swallowed up and people find themselves living to work, rather than working to live. This is an unhealthy scenario which many counsellors and psychologists blame for the accelerating divorce and separation rate seen in our society today. Obviously dual careers can work, but it means both partners having to abandon traditional roles in order to adopt more flexible arrangements both at work and at home. This is never easy.

Employers' Obligations

There are, of course, statutory provisions which apply to stress in the workplace, but although employers are generally aware of their obligations as far as they relate to physical injury, far too few are yet aware that they now also have obligations regarding mental health. Stress has an effect on the mental health of employees as well as on their physical health, and both are covered by the duty of care which employers have towards their workforce. The Health and Safety Executive guidelines state that 'employers have a legal duty to take reasonable care to ensure that health is not placed at risk through excessive and sustained levels of stress arising from the way work is organised, the way people deal with each other at their work, or from the day to day demands placed on their workplace'. In other words, they state that 'stress should be treated like any other health hazard'.

The Main Sources of Work Stress

Most people encounter the same sort of problems at work, but each stress factor will vary in degree and significance, just as the employee's personality will determine how he or she will be affected. However, cumulative stress from certain commonly recognised sources will not only create hardships for the individual but also for the company in which he or she works. These hardships and their consequences are illustrated in the diagram on the following page which shows the importance of all these interrelated factors.

Amongst the problems most often cited as sources of workplace stress is the job itself. How many of the following problems do you recognise?

Work Overload
To employees this may mean either that they simply have too much work to do, or that the work that they are being asked to

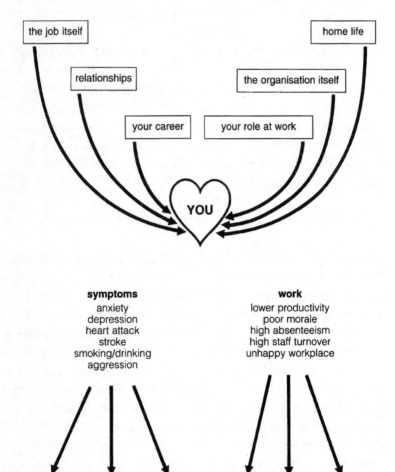

The causes and consequences of stress at work

do is too difficult for them. Common problems cited include having to work ridiculously long hours whilst having less time for leisure and the pursuit of a healthy lifestyle, all of which combine to promote stress-related illness.

New Technology

Very few workplaces have not been dramatically changed by the introduction of new technology in the last few years. It has meant that management and workers alike have had to adapt their working practices, their equipment and often their work-force itself in order to cope. This has resulted in enormous pressure for people to keep up to date with the new technology and to compete with others, not just in the immediate work-place, but against other companies too. For older employees, for whom change is usually the hardest, there is often a feeling of working as part of a machine, rather than as a human being. In addition, some forms of technology have brought about an increasing sense of isolation for many employees, such as lone bus drivers and assembly-floor workers.

Shift Working

Shift work undoubtedly suits some people, but for the vast majority it is a prime source of occupational stress. It inter-feres with the normal body clock so that sleeping problems are often experienced. The hours worked are often awkward and unsocial. Shift working has also been associated with a variety of alterations to normal body functioning. Research into air traffic controllers doing shift work, for example, showed four times the usual rate of high blood pressure, and more cases of diabetes and stomach ulcers than were found in a comparable group working nine to five. Shift work is particularly troublesome when it is irregular, so that the body clock never gets a chance to adjust.

Time Pressures and Deadlines

Jobs which necessitate working to strict deadlines are innately stressful. Time pressure always evokes a sense of urgency, and the level of stress arousal is always high in workers who have to meet tight deadlines for every task, such as those who work in the print media. One of the reasons why Type A personalities suffer so much stress is because they are prone to setting themselves unrealistic and unnecessary deadlines.

Long Hours

Despite the advent of new technology, people are now working longer hours than they did twenty or thirty years ago. Most employees work at least two to three hours a week longer, and many managers are working twice that. Some people, such as junior hospital doctors, may work anything up to 100 hours a week, sometimes having no sleep for thirty-six hours or more. Unfortunately, working such long hours for the sake of experience, or for personal or financial reward, takes its toll. Younger people working more than forty-eight hours a week have been shown to have twice the risk of death from heart attack compared with similar people working only forty hours a week. Quite apart from that, it has been shown that working beyond fifty hours a week becomes increasingly unproductive anyway.

Travel and Commuting

Travelling abroad is often perceived as attractive and appealing to those who never get the chance to do it. But for many people who have to do it, it can be a significant source of stress. Domestic life can be seriously disrupted when the breadwinner spends large amounts of time away from home. Sitting in queues of traffic, waiting at airports and being unavoidably delayed because of transport problems can be tiresome. Very little opportunity usually exists to actually see the places visited and whilst the traveller is away from the office, a feeling of missing out, or being passed over for other opportunities, can arise.

Poor Working Conditions

Working in a cramped physical environment where we have little control over the temperature, the lighting, the noise or the equipment can certainly affect the way we feel. 'Sick building syndrome' is a term which has been used to describe a range of symptoms in employees who are made depressed and apathetic by their surroundings. Poorly designed offices where no natural light is present or where dim strip lighting is the predominant source of illumination are bad enough, but mismatched desks and chairs, different pieces of equipment at different eye levels and haphazard distribution of personnel all contribute. The belief that colds, coughs and other viral symptoms are propagated by air conditioning systems is endemic and the phrase 'something certainly seems to be doing the rounds in the office' is becoming something of a cliché. More attention has been paid recently to the importance of office ergonomics. This is to be welcomed, especially if all working environments come to be treated in the same way.

Working Just for the Money

'Take the money and run' is the advice given to anybody who is unhappy in their work. It is symptomatic of a major source of stress and takes us back to the old philosophy that we all have to work in order to survive, and for no other reason. Where people work just for the money, they do not feel valued or appreciated and there is a lack of fulfilment or satisfaction.

Poor Pay

Being poorly paid is not necessarily stressful in itself, although most people would rather be wealthy and stressed than hard-up and stressed. Financial insecurity certainly contributes to cumulative stress at work if the level of job satisfaction does not make up for a low salary.

Boredom

Some jobs are inherently boring. Many machines have rendered already mundane jobs even more tedious, and workers are often controlled in their working patterns by the pace and capacity of the machine. Everybody, however, needs variety, interest and a degree of social support. Job rotation, job sharing, job enlargement, and more flexible working arrangements and shift patterns can all help alleviate boredom.

Relationships at Work

Another major source of work stress is to be found in the area of relationships at work. The various interactions we all have with other people may either be a source of great stress or great support. We are fortunate if we work in a creative and effective team where humour features large, everybody is treated as an equal, and there is mutual respect and under-standing. But many of us have to work for people we hate and do not respect, and where hostility from other colleagues or confrontations with members of the public are part and parcel of the job. The way we relate to our bosses and our subordinates significantly affects the way we feel at the end of each day and each working week. This is a major considera-tion in both personal health and in the productivity of any company or industry.

Relationships with Your Immediate Boss
Psychological studies have shown that a considerate boss is more likely to foster easy relationships built on trust, respect, warmth and friendship. Where the boss appears not to care or show any understanding, workers report feeling under more pressure. Stressful situations include unconstructive criticism, favouritism and pulling rank.

Relationships with Underlings
Office politics happen in almost every place of work, and personality clashes, suspicion and competition between co-workers is only natural. When a bad atmosphere is allowed to fester, however, and where resentment and paranoia breed, it is bad for the well-being of both the individual and the company as a whole. Type A people who push themselves to the limit and who are abrasive and ruthless ignore not only their own feelings but those of others around them, breeding an atmosphere of tension and hostility.

On the other hand, good working relationships with colleagues can provide a supportive social network where difficulties at work can be discussed and resolved. Mutually considerate workers, headed by a person-orientated manager, are much less likely to whinge and exaggerate the problems, and are more likely to tackle them for the benefit of all concerned.

Relationships with Clients or Members of the Public
People whose work involves close contact with large numbers of people, such as the police, nurses or care workers, often report high levels of stress. This is particularly true if they are unsuited to handling personal problems or have had no training in how to do so. Confrontations with the public can be pressurised, particularly if they involve large numbers of people and are a persistent feature of the job.

Sexual Harassment

When relationships at work are soured by sexism or sexual harassment life for the victim can become very difficult indeed. It is particularly awkward and threatening if the harassment is coming from a superior, or if it is difficult to avoid situations where the trouble crops up. It is vital to be assertive in this situation and to make it absolutely clear right from the start that not only are the advances unwelcome, but they are offensive and upsetting. It is well worth discreetly asking fellow colleagues' if they have ever suffered the same experience, either in the past or more recently and keeping a daily diary of events, conversations and situations as they arise, in case they are needed for future legal reference. Ultimately, a formal complaint may have to be made, and the law now offers effective and available protection for victims of this insidious form of bullying.

At a medical practice where I myself was a doctor, the partners wanted to show our staff that we were aware of the importance of such issues and we asked them about their opinions regarding sexual harassment. 'There isn't enough of it' came the reply, much to everyone's amusement. Such refreshing humour, however, is not always appropriate or appreciated in a setting where harassment is taking place. Managers who claim that there is no problem at their workplace are probably either unaware that it is occurring or, frankly, are just not interested in doing anything about it.

Career Development

For many people in today's employment climate, career development takes second place to whether one has a job at all, or for how long. The ideal situation of plenty of job security, and steady progress towards promotion and better remuneration, is relatively rare. A much more common scenario is one of total lack of job security, with constant rumours about impending redundancy and regular, rather worrying performance-related audits. Unwanted retirement and unattained ambitions, particularly when they involve being passed over for a younger colleague, all produce frustration, tension and stress.

Job Security
Most people are prepared to put up with persistent hassles when they first start a job, knowing that they can expect better pay and a chance of promotion prospects as they gain experience and maturity within their workplace. By the time middle age comes along, however, career development slows down, new opportunities are reduced in number, new technology takes longer to get to grips with, and enthusiasm and drive begin to flag as younger more vigorous competitors from below start coming through. Even professional jobs, which were once considered jobs for life, no longer offer guaranteed security. Hospital consultants, civil servants and members of the armed forces are all no longer able to count on long-term job security.

Job Appraisal
Being judged, examined and evaluated in the work which we do can be a threatening and worrying experience for many of us. The person performing the appraisal knows that they may be having a direct effect on the livelihood and self-esteem of the person concerned, and also that should their assessment be challenged, they could themselves be the subject of some form of grievance procedure.

Promotion and Demotion
Demotion is obviously stressful, but even promotion may be welcome or unwelcome. Some people are entirely happy to

stay at the same level of work capacity if they find it suits them whereas others may be promoted without the desire or the skills to take on the additional responsibilities and demands.

Staff Motivation

Most people would agree that some companies are better to work for than others. No one wants to feel like just another cog in a giant wheel, and most workers want the opportunity to participate and feel that their abilities are valued. This kind of dissatisfaction only results in depression, apathy, absenteeism and a rapid staff turnover. Individuals are much more likely to abuse alcohol and other drugs as an escape from the drudgery of dead-end work. However, where companies encourage personnel to participate in making decisions, or even to profit share, there is a tremendous sense of investment in the company's success, a feeling of belonging, and a commitment to better rapport and communication throughout the organisation. Large corporations, notably in Sweden, Japan and the United States, who were among the first to create this kind of atmosphere in their workplaces, have replicated their success in their factories in Britain where strikes and industrial action have been dramatically reduced.

Not Knowing What is Expected of You

Life is much less stressful at work when you know what is expected of you, and where your role is clearly defined. Uncertainty and vulnerability lead to stress, decreased motivation and a certain restlessness which usually results in seeking another job.

Conflicting Duties

Some jobs entail having to do things which are unpopular with the workforce, or which may not be considered part of the usual job. Supervisors, for example, can be torn between having to please their bosses but also keeping their subordinates happy and under control. Technology-orientated managers are often not very good at handling people, and those with high levels of anxiety tend to suffer more than others as a result of such conflicts.

The Burden of Responsibilities

One of the hardest responsibilities in any job is looking after other people. This is usually much more stressful than being in charge of material things, such as the buildings themselves, the equipment housed within them, or budgets. It is hard for workers facing redundancy in the cost-cutting climate that we now face, but managers also suffer from having to juggle the responsibilities of trimming costs to a minimum whilst at the same time attempting to look after the workforce as best they can.

The Culture Within the Workplace

An individual's role in any company becomes more assured and satisfying if trouble has been taken to recruit the right people and build a good team. Workers are less likely to feel stressed if their job is fully explained to them, and any possible risks involved in the job are made clear from the outset. A supportive rather than a confrontational atmosphere at work is important, and continuous training, job rotation, job sharing and flexibility will give rise to cohesion and co-operation.

Homelife

Traditionally, coming home from work was synonymous with relaxation and peace. It was a place of support and encouragement. But in the current economic climate, where employment is precious, job security is under threat and working hours are longer, more and more is being asked of individual employees. Many of us are under increasing pressure to take work home with us and rely even more heavily on family members to co-operate with us despite the fact that we are hardly ever there. Another major source of stress is the prospect of relocation allied to promotion, which means a major upheaval for the family as a whole. It involves significant changes to the family's economic, educational and cultural future. Despite being a major decision in any family's life, there are precious few facilities, even in the biggest and most forward-thinking organisations, to enable these decisions to be made to everyone's satisfaction.

Homelife can be further threatened by the increasing trend towards dual career families. In Britain nearly sixty-five percent of all women go out to work now, and more than half of them work full time. Just like their male counterparts, they need support and understanding at home. When neither partner is able to provide support for the other, relationships are more likely to come under strain. Few men, even in today's more liberated society, are really prepared to work the double shift involved in managing the home as well as the job, and 'new man' has not really materialised. The accelerating, and alarming divorce rate in the UK, in the States and in other Western European countries in the last decade, may very largely have been precipitated by the influence of employment on home life.

The Cost of Stress in the Workplace

There is now overwhelming evidence that excessive stress at work imposes enormous costs on individuals and industry alike. The Confederation of British Industry (CBI) calculated in 1995 that alcohol-related problems alone account for 1.7

billion pounds a year and 8 million working days lost. Heart disease and strokes cost a further 62 million working days lost, and mental disorders 91 million days at a cost of 3.7 billion pounds. The British Heart Foundation estimates that heart disease costs an average British company with 10,000 employees, 73,000 working days per year, 2.5 million pounds in lost productivity, and the actual lives of forty-two of its workers between the ages of thirty-five and sixty-four. MIND, the mental health charity, attributes about thirty-five percent of all sick leave to psychological and emotional problems. Whilst there is a widespread belief that top executives with Type A personalities are the ones most at risk of heart attack, statistics actually show the opposite. Skilled manual workers have two and a half times the death rate from heart disease compared with that of managers, and middle managers have a forty percent greater chance of dying from a heart attack than top executives. In addition, manual workers generally die younger than white collar staff, and unskilled workers are more at risk than others of dying from cancer, heart failure and chronic chest disease. Interestingly, their non-working wives and partners seem to follow the same pattern, with their medical problems mirroring those of their working partners.

The indirect costs to industry of workplace stress are also seen in terms of larger numbers of accidents at work, strike problems, rapid staff turnover, high absenteeism, and poor quality control. But rather than taking steps to try and reduce the incidence of these factors, many companies regard these problems simply as an inevitable part of being in business. It is the National Health Service which is left to pick up the bill.

Companies are now beginning to acknowledge that they would actually get their money back within a small number of years by taking measures to deal with workplace stress effectively. They are also coming under much more legal pressure to prevent themselves falling foul of worker compensation laws which are designed to protect employees from 'cumulative trauma'. Several recent cases have awarded substantial damages to employees who suffered from stress-related disorders where the stress was both 'foreseeable' and 'unwarranted'.

How is Your Employer Looking After You?

Just how companies can cut the enormous costs of stress in the workplace is addressed in Chapter 10, but how do you know if, at the present time, your organisation is looking after you? Ask yourself the following questions.

1. Are you having to put in a lot of extra hours, take work home with you, or work part of the weekend just to keep up with the volume of work?

2. Do you find that your work often interferes with your personal or family life?

3. Is there a lot of back stabbing, bad temper and irritability in your workplace, especially amongst junior members of staff?

4. Are you asked to comply with decisions and changes imposed from above, without any warning or discussion?

5. Does management show little interest in understanding workers' problems?

If you answer yes to only one of these questions, there are already significant signs of stress. Problems like these are often attributed to the recession and to cost-cutting manoeuvres, but there are still adjustments which can be made to improve things even in a poor economic climate. The real fault is more likely to lie in poor management than anything else.

How Satisfying is Your Job?

People are always stunned when the winner of the National Lottery turns up for work as usual on the Monday morning despite their windfall. In fact, when a large number of people were questioned in a survey, more than fifty percent said that they would continue to work even if they could well afford not to. Clearly, employment has a benefit to the individual over and above the financial rewards. It gives a purpose and a meaning to life that can be enriching and satisfying. However, there are plenty of people who really do work just for the money and whose working day is nothing but drudgery. Not everyone feels secure in a well-organised company where the work is interesting and their promotional prospects are good. Not everyone brings home a decent salary, gets on with their working colleagues, is happy with their working hours and conditions and has just the right amount of responsibility and freedom in which to work. In fact, there are plenty of people who are unhappy with their work, but who are they? Judging by sick leave statistics, job stress generally increases as job status and skill level diminishes. But working in a lowly position with little challenge is by no means stressful for everybody. People who are happy anyway, and have little to excite or stimulate them, will tend to feel relaxed. People who are unhappy or dissatisfied because of lack of challenges, on the other hand, are likely to feel depressed. The same unhappy people when given lots to do are likely to feel anxious, whereas workers who are content and rise to the challenge of extra work can feel invigorated and cheerful. To find out whether your job is stressful, ask yourself the following questions.

1. Do you feel challenged and stretched by your work?

2. Are you appreciated and respected?

3. Are you using all your abilities and skills to their best possible advantage?

4. Do you have pride in a product that is being developed?

5. Are you involved in decision making?

6. Do you have a hand in solving problems?

7. Is there plenty of variety at work?

8. Is there an opportunity to take frequent breaks?

If the answer to just one of these questions was no, then there is already a climate for potential job stress.

How Stressful is Your Job?

Try answering the questionnaire at the end of this chapter on page 126. This should help you to identify how satisfied you are with your own job and how stressful you find it.

The stress which any individual perceives at work depends on many factors, but not least on their own personality and the job–worker fit. Not everybody is suited to any particular job. Librarians who are methodical but introverted are often considered to have low stress ratings at work, but their job satisfaction is often high. An extrovert personality, however, who is bored stiff cooped up amidst rows and rows of dusty volumes could feel highly stressed and highly dissatisfied with their job.

Are You in the Right Job for You?

Some people have aimlessly drifted into the wrong job by chance. Many of us have to make important decisions when we are far too young, for example about examination subjects, before we have really made up our minds what we want as a career in the future. Others have been pushed into a job at the bidding of their parents and discover, much later in life, that they are better suited to a completely different type of employment than the one in which they are currently working.

Jobs also evolve and alter in a changing economic and technological climate. One motor mechanic I know had been entirely happy for more than thirty years in his job at the same garage until he was asked by his newly appointed managers to dishonestly cut down on the amount of warranty work done for customers. He found the burden of guilt, and the responsibility for denying customers their rights and entitlements, far too much of a burden and became quite depressed and anxious as a result. Other people have been unwillingly promoted or demoted into the wrong job. You may have been in your job for so long that you no longer know whether it is the right job for you or not. If you are unsure, try asking yourself the following questions.

1. Are others around you much happier than you are?

2. Do you think the employment suits your temperament?

3. Are you good at handling people or would you rather be 'tinkering' with things and objects?

4. Are you doing the job just because it is secure? Security is all very well, but it can also be a trap whereby you are held

in a job you hate and denied the excitement of finding work in an area that you would find more fulfilling.

5. What is it you loathe about your job, and what is it you love about your hobbies and pastimes? Could you find a more satisfying job working in those areas related to your real loves?

If you still have any doubts about whether you are in the right job, keep a stress diary, making a note of all the things that make you fed up, depressed or anxious. Then consider exploring other career opportunities by talking to occupational consultants, or simply looking around at what others are doing.

One Man's Meat . . .

The green monster of envy often raises its ugly head when we look at other people's jobs. 'I would love to do their job,' we say without knowing the pressures and pitfalls associated with it. At the same time we look at menial jobs and turn up our noses in disgust at the things employees less fortunate than ourselves have to do. But I know of at least one waste disposal labourer who was totally satisfied with his job, and at least one TV presenter who simply hated hers. 'Don't you mind the smell?' the sewage engineer was often asked as he climbed down the ladder into another customer's septic tank. 'No, don't notice it to tell you the truth,' he would say with a grin before proceeding with his work. Since then, he has gone on to set up his own very successful business. The TV presenter on the other hand, performing in a job which millions aspire to, hated the hours worked and what she considered the insincerity of it all. She is still doing it, through gritted teeth, but only because it pays well – another example of somebody in the job just for the money. I'm not suggesting that these two personalities should swap jobs. It is far more complex than that, but there are jobs with both high and low salaries which are more or less challenging, which are more or less dangerous, and which are at the cutting edge of change to a greater or lesser degree. The trick is to find the job which gives you just the right amount of stress to keep you on your toes, and just the right amount of satisfaction to keep you interested.

Different Roles, Different Stresses

The problems you experience in your job will no doubt differ according to the level you are at in the company hierarchy.

If you are a Manager or Supervisor

If you are a supervisor or manager you might experience a high degree of role conflict in that you have to try to please the boss on the one hand and subordinates on the other. You have to decide where your primary responsibility lies. You also need to be able to delegate work appropriately, without interfering with that work once you have allocated it. Subordinates should be kept informed about any matters which affect them and confidences, of course, should always be kept. It is still possible to please the boss whilst protecting subordinates' interests, as well as being aware and considerate about any of their personal problems. If they are given feedback and praise for what they do well, they will be better motivated to do a better job for you. Problems generally occur when subordinates are told what to do without explanation, rather than negotiating the best plan of action with their help and input, and then sharing the rewards with them.

Junior Staff

If you are a member of a company's junior staff, remember that employees working under a supervisor should not be subordinate in every possible way. There is still a need to query orders if they are ambiguous and to use your own initiative where required. Constructive criticism is useful, and it is satisfying to put forward and justify your own creative ideas. Enthusiasm for new projects is always appreciated and any complaints should be made to superiors rather than fellow workers. Otherwise this just whips up a bad atmosphere of disaffection all round. It goes without saying that the workload should be shared out as equally as possible, and that everyone needs to be co-operative when it comes to keeping noise levels down and sharing space, light and the best of the available equipment. It is a big mistake to sound off about another fellow worker to superiors, and although it sounds obvious to have to point it out, taking your turn to fetch the tea and coffee is something which is noticed perhaps more than anything else by equal colleagues. If you do not do your share, other people will certainly talk about you!

If you are Self-employed or Free to Choose Your Own Way of Working

Perhaps you are lucky enough to be able to exercise a great deal of freedom in the way you work. That is fine, but you will have your own particular problems too however, especially if you tend towards being a Type A personality. If this is the case, you need to establish your priorities as much as possible. If tasks can be categorised as either immediate tasks requiring urgent attention, or more long-term projects, this helps in planning. It is also useful to draw up a list of jobs which you are postponing because they are unpleasant and unpopular. Putting off until tomorrow what should be done today is inevitably stressful in itself and can make you feel unsettled and restless. If the awful jobs are done first, you can then enjoy a pleasant, sociable lunch as a reward before working through the rest of the list later on in the day.

Some items on your list of things to do will crop up time and time again, in which case they might as well be crossed off as they clearly are no longer important. On the other hand, if you are always behind and can never quite catch up you should stop to consider your workload and the way you are dealing with it. Talk to your immediate superior about the problems. It is simply not good enough to accept every job that is thrown your way just because you are being paid. Neither is it the case that you are simply in the wrong job, because it could very well just be the way you are doing it, or the amount you are being asked to do.

Are you a Workaholic?

How many of the Type A personality characteristics do you display? Ask yourself the following questions and tot up the number of times you answer yes.

1. Do you find it hard to say no when given extra work?

2. Do you feel that if you want a job done well, you should do it yourself?

3. Do you work long hours willingly?

4. Do you take your work home most days?

5. Do you often think about problems at work when you are at home?

6. Does your work ever keep you awake at night?

7. Do your family or friends say they hardly ever see you because you are always working?

8. Is going on holiday a real hassle because of work commitments either just before or just after vacation?

9. Do you feel bad and self-critical if things are not going well at work?

10. Do you become easily irritated or angry over trivial things?

Surprisingly enough, if you have answered yes to just two of the questions above, you are becoming just a little bit too involved with work for your own good and unable to live your life independently around it. You could easily become a workaholic if you are not careful.

If you have answered yes to more than three questions, you are already addicted to work. The more yes answers you gave, the more of a workaholic you are. You need to look at what is important for you in your life now, not only for the sake of your health and career, but also for your family's security, and your relationship with your partner and your friends. Ultimately, the career path which you are following and to which you have devoted yourself so obsessively will also soon suffer, if you do not take steps to modify your behaviour.

Special Problems of the Caring Professions

Individuals working within the caring professions, or for that matter as unpaid carers in the home, face special stress-related problems. They have been termed 'emotional labourers' because theirs is largely a role of giving rather than receiving love, support, care and affection. The cost of such unrequited generosity of spirit is high, despite the initial job satisfaction. Problems of emotional burnout featuring increasing apathy, cynicism and selfishness are commonly seen. People affected by this may find it difficult to establish and maintain normal social relationships. You only have to look at the stormy social life of the characters in the BBC's *Casualty* to know what I mean. This may be a medical soap opera, but there is a large element of truth in it.

Another problem of burnout is that it encourages escapist drug abuse with people smoking more, drinking more and generally punishing themselves in other anti-social ways. The life expectancy of nurses, believe it or not, is four years less than the average working woman, and the suicide rate amongst doctors, psychiatrists and dentists is more than twice the national average. The kinds of jobs affected, however, are not just nurses and doctors, or social workers and other employees in health care, but teachers, librarians, waiters, secretaries, and receptionists, among others. Low status and pay are common to them all, and many of them also work in isolation, fending off demanding clients in a situation where there is little support or worker involvement, and where there is no clear criteria of success in the job performed. Career prospects are usually non-existent or very poor, or their career may reach a plateau when they are still relatively young. The job is usually secure, although less so these days, but the feeling of being stuck in a dead-end job where little appreciation is received, is immensely stressful.

With an increasing tendency towards bureaucratic cost-cutting, the needs of people involved in the caring professions are often sacrificed on the altar of financial necessity. But a few simple measures could do much to give people a sense of 'belonging' and to bolster the services provided. Good communication between the employees in different areas of the caring services is important and can be achieved with little cost. Feedback of employees' problems should be speedy and effective. Ill-defined, faceless hierarchies making painfully slow decisions can be the kiss of death for many employees, so moves should be made to keep decision making as transparent as possible, or at least to separate the organisation into smaller groups with properly democratic functions. Retraining is vital to keep employees up to date and to enable them to share and participate. It also serves to give them some breathing space and an opportunity to boost their flagging morale. Finally, unions and individual workers need to push hard for political recognition of the importance of their jobs, and to protect and maintain job status, salary and working conditions. It is surely not right that the society which pays the bosses of privatised industry hundreds of thousands of pounds allows carers in the home to look after the sick, the disabled or the terminally ill at such personal and emotional cost, for a few pounds a week. We should remember that the cost to the state of taking on such work would be a great deal more.

Special Problems of Working Women
Since the early 1970s, women who do not go out to work have become the minority, and sixty-five percent of all women now work, half of whom are working full time. But despite progressive emancipation and the advent of equal opportunities and better anti-discrimination laws, women still tend to find themselves in the lower-paid industries, either working from home or working part time. If that was not bad enough, they suffer from the same sources of stress which men experience, in addition to discrimination, sexism and the entrenched attitudes of certain male colleagues and bosses.

For many women stress can begin as soon as they start in a job. When they do not conform to the usual sexual stereotype they can easily, yet unknowingly, become a threat to a male colleague whose reaction can be one of resentment or anger. Most working women are also mothers these days and so as well as a full day at work, they are still expected to fetch the shopping, do the housework, and perform the traditional caring role of preparing the meals and looking after the family's health.

A typical working woman's day, therefore, is nearer twelve to fourteen hours than the usual eight hours of a nine to five shift. The conditions in which women work also frequently mean that they are either in total social isolation or, like two-thirds of them, working in a female-only environment. Dual career families face additional pressures. Where the woman earns a wage which is designed to supplement the family income, things are not so bad. But when her salary is equal to, or greater than, that of her male partner, conflict can arise because of the threat to the male's self-esteem and because of the inevitable controversy over the division of domestic responsibilities.

Women in any of these kinds of situation may find the following simple guidelines helpful in keeping stress to a minimum.

1. Communicate fully with your partner so that you are both clear about what you want from your working and home lives.

2. Bear in mind that whatever each individual wishes to accomplish, it will have an effect on your partner's freedom and choices as a result.

3. Make long-term future plans together to keep arguments to a minimum.

4. Separate your domestic and working lives by establishing strict boundaries and cut-off periods. This should not stop you communicating your fears, challenges and rewards from work with your partner, however. Effective communication is always to be encouraged.

5. Rather than devote yourself to a particular company or industry, keep your career plans centred on yourself. That means being willing to retrain, learn new skills, move house etc.

6. Make sure that both you and your partner limit your ambitions in order to give each other freedom and opportunity as well as sufficient leisure time together and with the family.

Are you a true career woman?

Conflict is always more likely if you are a true career woman whose desires and ambitions come before the needs and expectations of your partner or family. To find out just how much of a committed career woman you are, ask yourself the following questions.

1. Do you usually describe yourself by the job that you do?

2. Do you regard your job as being more important than your husband's?

3. Would you be unhappy to contemplate taking on a less challenging job, even if the needs of your family demanded it?

4. Does your partner have a lower level of formal education than you?

5. Do you find you have little time to support your partner in his own employment?

6. Did you ignore any thoughts of having a family in the future when you chose your career?

If the answer to any of these questions is no then you are probably ambivalent about the career you have chosen, and it is likely that you and your partner have a fairly equal attitude to your relationship and ambitions. However, five yes answers, diagnoses you as being a fully fledged career woman and nothing, not even the family, is likely to hold you back. To discover where your partner stands in this situation ask yourself the following questions.

1. Is he happy to earn less than you, or would he be?

2. Does he do all he can to help you with the chores at home as well as your own career?

3. Is he genuinely thrilled at your abilities and achievements?

4. Would he be willing to put his own career on hold to advance yours?

5. Is he content for you to delegate the household duties to others, including him?

If your partner answers yes to more than three or four of these questions, and the answers are genuinely honest, then you are a fortunate woman. You are living with a 'new-ish' man. If only one or two apply, then he is probably ambivalent about your success and possibly rather threatened as well. You are living with an old traditionalist, I'm afraid.

Special Problems of the Self-Employed
Working for oneself can be satisfying in many ways but there are a considerable number of additional responsibilities to face, and these can prove particularly stressful. People starting out on their own, however, are often only capable of seeing the advantages. These include:

- choosing the hours that you work;
- choosing how much holiday to take and when;
- selecting what kind of work you wish to do;

- having no one else to answer to;
- not being held back by the incompetence or inadequacy of others;
- being able to benefit from certain tax allowances; and
- being generally in control of your own destiny.

This is likely to sound attractive if you are slaving away in a thankless job, covering for a clueless boss who steals your best creative ideas and then takes all the credit for them. But many an employee, only mildly dissatisfied with their secure nine to five job on PAYE, has regretted making the bold step of throwing it all away to become self-employed. This is what happened in Frank's case.

Having unrealistic expectations
Frank was a thirty-five-year-old carpenter whose skills were highly thought of in the building trade. He had worked for just two major construction firms in his working lifetime, and whilst being reasonably well looked after with promotion and modest salary hikes, he still had to supplement his wages by doing backbreaking overtime. In addition, he was now expected to train up new, somewhat unenthusiastic apprentices and supervise and correct their work when necessary. Whenever a job warranted special expertise and experience the company relied on Frank to provide it. At first this flattered and stimulated him but in recent years, especially when no particular rewards, bonuses or even gratitude came his way, he began to feel used. He was saving the company thousands of pounds in outside consultancy fees which would otherwise prove necessary. At the same time he was having to turn down an increasing amount of private work he was offered in his spare time, work he was asked to do by personal recommendation and reputation. With the encouragement of his wife he

took the plunge, resigned from the company and became self-employed.

Initially, there was sufficient work to keep him fully occupied and to meet his overheads. The bank manager was reluctant to lend him money for plant equipment and tools until he had either proved himself or provided a business plan. Frank had no idea what he meant. Work soon picked up, however, and he enjoyed a six-month period of complete satisfaction. Towards the end of this time he could not resist taking on every contract offered him because, as he said, 'I've got to say yes because you just never know how long it will last'. Before he knew it, he was totally snowed under and things started to go really wrong. He started getting complaints that jobs were not adequately finished; people never paid up promptly when invoices were due; subcontractors who were paid to do the bricklaying, mixing cement, and providing essential materials let him down. One day, while exasperatedly shifting several hundredweight of hardcore himself, he slipped a disc in his back and was incapacitated. Because he had made little or no provision for this eventuality, things went from bad to worse. He lost his house, became seriously depressed and the entire family suffered financially and socially.

Frank's story is certainly not unique, and the tragedy is that if his particular skills had been allied to a better organised plan of action he might have done very well. He certainly became all too aware of the very real disadvantages of becoming self-employed. These include:

- having either too little or too much work to cope with at any one time;
- having no guarantee of regular income;
- having to manage your own accounts;

- running into difficulty through ill-health;
- having to pay your own National Insurance contributions whilst receiving only basic state benefits in return;
- knowing that holidays, weekends and other leisure breaks mean less money coming in; and
- feeling pressured to postpone or avoid leisure time.

How to Reduce the Stress of Self-Employment
Provided you are aware of the benefits and drawbacks of this kind of employment, it is quite possible to flourish under its constraints. Indeed, the satisfaction and sense of freedom that come from successfully setting up on your own can be immense. So remember the golden rules for ensuring that you are ready for self-employment.

1. Establish a realistic and achievable work plan setting out aims, priorities, timescales, cash flow, a schedule for buying tools and machinery, and contingency plans for backup.

2. Decide on the hours you wish to work and stick to them.

3. Decide what type of work you will and will not accept.

4. Decide what salary you are aiming for.

5. Be realistic and say no to commitments which threaten your work plan or encroach on your time with family and other leisure time.

6. Put time for important social events firmly in your diary.

7. Keep on top of your accounts at all times including cashflow, VAT and income tax.

8. Put income aside to cover unforseen eventualities including sickness and invalidity.

9. Consider taking out long-term insurance policies to guard against the above.

Finally, never forget that when you are self-employed your health and well-being is even more important than when you were an employee. So enjoy a healthy lifestyle, and take on board all the stress-busting tips listed in the chapters to follow.

Questionnaire: How Satisfying or Stressful is Your Job?

Give yourself a point for every feature of your job with which you are satisfied. Then give yourself a separate score between 0 and 5 for the amount of stress you experience with each of the job features, where 0 is no stress whatsoever, 1 is mildly stressed, 2 is moderately stressed, 3 is highly stressed, 4 is extremely stressed, and 5 is crisis point.

	Job Feature	Satisfying	Stress Level
1.	Commuting to work	Yes/No	0 1 2 3 4 5
2.	The workplace environment ie heating, lighting, noise, ventilation, work stations etc.	Yes/No	0 1 2 3 4 5
3.	The number of hours worked	Yes/No	0 1 2 3 4 5
4.	The amount of variety in the job	Yes/No	0 1 2 3 4 5
5.	The security of the job	Yes/No	0 1 2 3 4 5
6.	Knowing what is going on (communication)	Yes/No	0 1 2 3 4 5
7.	Interest in the job	Yes/No	0 1 2 3 4 5
8.	Freedom to choose the way you work	Yes/No	0 1 2 3 4 5
9.	Freedom to do the job in your own way	Yes/No	0 1 2 3 4 5
10.	The relationship with your co-workers	Yes/No	0 1 2 3 4 5
11.	Praise you receive for satisfactory work	Yes/No	0 1 2 3 4 5
12.	Having more than one immediate superior	Yes/No	0 1 2 3 4 5
13.	Your salary	Yes/No	0 1 2 3 4 5
14.	The chances you have to use your skills and talents	Yes/No	0 1 2 3 4 5
15.	Relationship between management and workers in your workplace	Yes/No	0 1 2 3 4 5
16.	Your chances of promotion	Yes/No	0 1 2 3 4 5
17.	The way the company is run	Yes/No	0 1 2 3 4 5
18.	Consideration that is paid to suggestions you make	Yes/No	0 1 2 3 4 5
19.	The need to take work home with you	Yes/No	0 1 2 3 4 5
20.	The intrusion of work into your home life	Yes/No	0 1 2 3 4 5

Self-assessment

Job satisfaction

If you are satisfied with more than fifty percent of the features in your job, you are doing well. A third of the British population claim to be dissatisfied with their work but precious few of the remaining two-thirds would be able to say that they score one hundred percent in the job satisfaction stakes.

Stress rating

A score of 50 or above indicates that your stress levels at work are too high for all the wrong reasons. There are too many aspects of your job which, due to circumstances beyond your own control, are not increasing your productivity and are certainly not making your life any easier. If you score less than 10 on the job satisfaction scale, and more than 50 on the stress rating scale, then it might simply be time to look for another job.

CHAPTER TEN

WHAT YOUR EMPLOYER CAN DO FOR YOU

All of us need to be aware of the sources and effects of excess stress in our daily lives. Later sections of this book show how you can learn to do that, and give tips to help you manage stress more effectively. Considering the fact that a large proportion of the stress which we all suffer is generated in the workplace, it seems incredible that employers do not manage their business resources and personnel better. Stress takes a terrible toll in lost working days, reduced productivity, and absenteeism due to ill-health, so there is certainly already enough incentive to do something about it.

A few enlightened organisations have already seen the light by taking steps to boost morale, improve working conditions, and incorporate stress awareness and stress management courses into their business plan. Many of these companies have subsequently flourished in a climate where industry is generally under threat. New technology, staff down-sizing, fierce external competition, short-term contracts, and flatter company structures across the board have all increased stress levels enormously. At the same time, employees are being asked to produce more and perform better, with fewer and fewer resources.

Why Employers are Slow to Help

Traditionally, the attitude within management in British industry has been of the stiff upper lip variety. Few see very much wrong with the adage 'when the going gets tough, the tough get going'. They believe the unpleasant effects of stress come with the territory, and that if employees cannot stand the heat they should simply get out of the kitchen. They regard 'stress' as nothing more than a fashionable and passing fad, a syndrome manipulated by the weak to excuse and mitigate their feelings. They cannot understand how our recent predecessors managed to endure two world wars, the horrific depression of the 1930s, appalling working conditions, blatant exploitation and rampant disease, and yet never resorted to blaming how they felt on stress! Stress has always been there, of course, in another form, but the evidence does suggest that today's pressures and demands have increased whilst our coping abilities and skills have not been able to keep pace. Regrettably, only a small minority of enlightened firms and companies in Britain have invested in effective stress management programmes. These tend to be the larger, wealthier corporations, often taking their lead from their successful international counterparts.

It is time for top executives and senior managers themselves to become 'stress-aware' and to be willing to enthusiastically incorporate stress-busting policies into their organisations. Unfortunately, it is often top-flight management who are the most resistant to change and, without their involvement, attempts at stress relief in the working environment can become a struggle in itself.

Interestingly, even where companies have taken steps to make the necessary changes, their motives have not always been altruistic. Directors have long taken the rather cynical view that employing 'stressologists' to counter potential problems in the workplace is highly unlikely to boost company profits. They believe that once workers have had a few counselling sessions they might well decide that the best way towards self-improvement is to resign! That is hardly in the company's interests. Directors also calculate that the cost of establishing formal programmes to reduce stress at work might take ten to fifteen years to recoup, with little tangible benefit to show for it. They also fear opening a can of worms, since numerous and varied difficulties at work might be identified in the absence of any motivation, resources or ability to tackle them.

Why Employers are Changing their Tune

Things are gradually changing, however. One of the greatest new incentives to encourage employers to become stress-aware is the fact that their legal responsibilities towards employees are becoming clearer. In 1994 Chris Walker, an area social services manager, won a landmark case against his employers, Northumberland County Council, when the judge found the council guilty of breaching its duty of care to him. Mr Walker had suffered two nervous breakdowns, generated in part at least by his unfair and unrealistic workload. A few months later Chris Johnstone, a junior hospital doctor, was awarded an out-of-court settlement from Bloomsbury Health Authority after claiming that the unreasonable number of hours he worked on duty threatened his health. When you stop to consider that nearly all junior hospital doctors work similarly unsocial and protracted hours you wonder why the medical consultants for whom they work, and who should know all about the consequences of working such excessive hours, had not intervened earlier. 'It's the only way they learn and get experience' they generally say, 'and besides we had to do it in our time, so why shouldn't they?' You can begin to see why the handling of workplace stress changes so slowly, but at least it *is* changing.

The Institute of Personnel and Development believe that the management of every aspect of an organisation's human resources is as vital to the health and success of its business as the management of its capital and financial resources. Obviously, market forces ultimately influence just how well any industry performs but all things being equal, it is the investment in its employees that enables an organisation to achieve the very highest of standards and to maintain that leading edge over all other rivals. A caring company culture and the adoption of a systematic approach to occupational health are vital elements in the progress, development and success of any industrial enterprise.

In Germany, where the economy is generally considered to be the most successful in Europe, managers already know that working long hours does not necessarily lead to greater productivity. The average German manager usually works for shorter hours than his counterparts in other European countries. He is not impressed to see a subordinate working late, and far from admiring his colleague's devotion to his job, he is more likely to question his ability to get the job done in time, or to view his continued presence as a sign of insecurity. These managers do not make a habit of cancelling their holidays either, or of sacrificing the interests of their family for their work – they know that it is unhealthy.

In Scandinavia, employees are actually allowed to take five mental health days off from work each year. Where British employees telephone in to say they cannot come in because of backache, migraine or 'flu, in Scandinavia they simply ask for a mental health day instead. A survey carried out by British industry revealed that although ninety-four percent of British firms thought mental illness should be of concern to them, only ten percent had adopted any kind of company programme to deal with it. Of the ones that had, simply appointing a certain member of the existing staff to be responsible for picking up the telephone and dialling the GP seemed to be the proposed solution.

But now, at last, workplace health promotion is developing in Britain. This is good for employees, good for industry, and certainly cost-effective when practised with good resources and established expertise. And it is not only the large international corporations that are doing it. Contrary to popular belief, it can take place in much smaller organisations consisting of just a few members of staff.

How Employers Can Help Reduce Stress

Introduce Stress Audits

Firms and businesses cannot reasonably be expected to handle all of the sources of stress in their employees' private lives, but it is well worth them taking these into account when assessing them as individuals. One of the simplest forms of determining their level of stress is to set up specially designed stress audits, which consist of either surveys or questionnaires, and which can place a person on a stress rating scale. Having identified the sources of stress at work, the level of satisfaction, how the individual is coping with the problems, and their level of psychological and physical health, stress management training can then be instigated in order to get the very best out of each member of the workforce.

Stress audits, although mainly indicators of occupational stress, also serve to raise awareness of problems, and enable personnel to use positive thinking and creative problem-solving techniques to overcome any difficulties. Individuals can keep stress diaries to try to better locate particular sources of tension and smaller companies can also set up employee discussion groups to discuss issues such as job satisfaction and work scheduling, relationships at work, any communication difficulties, and employees' expectations and ambitions. In particular, any discomfort caused by the physical working conditions can be recognised.

Improve the Working Environment

The World Health Organisation has recognised 'sick building syndrome' since 1982, symptoms of which include a blocked nose, dry or sore eyes and throat, general fatigue and headache. Conditions which are often blamed include modern computerised offices with sealed windows and with ventilation and heating systems which employees have little or no ability to control. Other sources of irritation include high temperatures, stale air, glare and flicker from VDUs, excessive humidity, dust, chemical pollution and too little space in which to work.

Workers often erroneously believe that micro-organisms harboured in cooling systems are the root cause of all the colds, coughs and 'flu which permanently do the rounds. However, when staff make constructive comments about their working environment, it is appropriate for management to adopt a constructive attitude in return. This may not be sufficient to solve the problem but formal surveys and the assistance of building services engineers, occupational hygienists and psychologists often improve the situation. None of us nowadays work in the ghastly workhouses and sweatshops of the industrial revolution, but physical conditions at work today are still important.

Set up Occupational Health Departments

Occupational health departments can do a great deal to pick up signs of stress in employees. There are literally thousands of these throughout British industry and their success is largely dependent upon the enthusiasm and creativity of their staff. American Express in Brighton, for example, has a highly regarded occupational health department with full-time occupational health nurses and a visiting occupational health doctor. Employees have the use of a fully equipped gym and a range of health and stress management programmes available to all members of staff. The occupational health department recognises the importance of establishing good physical and psychological health, so they teach stress awareness and run programmes of stress management. They teach relaxation techniques even during working hours and also arrange counselling for a number of different problems. They discuss the need for lifestyle changes, give advice on how to stop smoking and how to reduce drinking, and offer help with dieting, as well as for screening for conditions such as coronary heart disease. Some of the services have occasionally been extended for the benefit of staff family members if required. When the nurses themselves, all of whom are trained counsellors, feel it is appropriate, more complex problems are often referred to specialists outside the company either in the NHS or privately at the company's expense.

Perhaps this model is one for other organisations to aspire to, but many corporations already run such departments. Even the House of Commons, renowned for the number of overweight, unhealthy-looking Members of Parliament under its roof can boast a Westminster gym which comprises a selection of aerobic equipment and free weights tailored for individual exercise, stress management and relaxation.

Stop Stress Before it Starts
It is possible to reduce potential levels of stress by recruiting individuals with particular care to ensure good job–worker fit.

This can be achieved through pre-employment medicals and appropriate psychometric testing. The latter is designed to match a person's skills, abilities, personality and temperament to the job they are being asked to do. It is also worth warning employees about the risks that their job may entail, for example long hours, urgent deadlines, being away from home, responsibility for budgets, and working in isolation. Companies can provide a supportive culture in which employees can work rather than an environment of confrontation. Jobs can be redesigned so that job sharing, job rotation, job flexibility and reasonable shift patterns are incorporated. Management style can be altered through training so that people are handled in a way that roots out bullying, discrimination and harassment. Policies to handle such behaviour should act as a firm deterrent.

People responsible for managing other people and their problems should learn to recognise stress and its warning signs in others, be it in their bosses or their subordinates. Since change and the need for adaptation is a major source of difficulties, fresh decisions should be adequately communicated to the workforce and retraining should be made available when needed. Grievance procedures should also be in place, and operationally effective, long before irreconcilable personality clashes and deep-seated resentments build up. As far as individuals themselves are concerned, occupational health departments can offer positive health promotion and preventative health care along the lines mentioned above.

Introduce Stress Education and Stress Management Techniques

Stress management techniques are very effective, provided they are taught by well qualified and experienced people with sufficient confidence and expertise. There is little point raising awareness of problems and making matters worse without being able to deal with them effectively and permanently. Stress management has been criticised in the past as a result of the plethora of untrained and inexperienced individuals who are able to advertise their services quite legally in *Yellow Pages* and similar publications. To combat this, the International Stress Management Association (ISMA) is now attempting to set up a register of validated counsellors in order to maintain high standards. Usually such help is offered only to white collar professionals to beat 'executive stress', but the basic techniques are the same and can be beneficial to all members of staff. The techniques usually incorporate biofeedback, exercise, relaxation, assertiveness training, time management, problem-solving skills, and general lifestyle advice and planning. The general concept is to make employees self-aware and to pre-empt the development of stress as a result. Hundreds of companies throughout the world have shown that such techniques work. Hopefully, they will be adopted by increasing numbers of organisations in Britain.

Make Counselling Available

Group-based training courses, as described above, are all very well for communicating general areas of malaise within a workforce, but where individual problems need to be addressed in further depth counselling is required. It can enable people to identify the reasons why they were conditioned to behave in certain ways at work, going right back to their childhood years. Employees with Type A behaviour can benefit in particular from such one-to-one counselling and make real strides towards changing the way they deal with stress.

The Association for Counselling at Work was first set up over ten years ago at a time when most employers were reluctant to pay for counsellors to handle employee stress, workplace whinging, or domestic disharmony. But the current economic climate has created an increasingly distressed and restless workforce. Some organisations such as the National Westminster Bank have responded accordingly and now employ an in-house network of occupational health advisers who can help employees in the traumatic aftermath of a bank raid as well as being an initial source of reference for anybody requiring ongoing counselling. Other organisations such as BP and Glaxo similarly employ specialist counsellors.

Set up an Employee Assistance Programme

Another innovation known as Employee Assistance Programmes, or EAPs, is swiftly gaining popularity. This import from the United States provides workers with a telephone hotline on which they can obtain support and advice on anything from how to pay a parking fine through to separation, divorce and moving house. About one million employees in Britain are already covered by such schemes and there are three reasons why these may become more popular in the future. To start with, employees are beginning to take their employers to court over stress-related illness at work, and companies obviously want to prevent this. Secondly, organisations have to pick up the cost of employees' sickness, and it has been estimated that forty percent of this is due to stress. Thirdly, increasing numbers of bosses are coming to understand that by helping workers cope with the changes which are happening in the workplace, and will continue to happen over the next decade, they will increase the health and outlook for their staff and maintain the competitiveness and performance of their company.

CHAPTER ELEVEN

YOU CAN RUN FROM STRESS BUT YOU CAN'T HIDE

Most people are blissfully unaware that they are suffering from the psychological or physical manifestation of stress. Just like Mark, one of the most stressed-out people I have ever met and the unwitting creator of the ironic title of this book, they cannot recognise the warning signs. They never have time to pause and reflect on why they are doing what they are doing or, for that matter, if they are doing it well or actually enjoying it. Their personal defence mechanisms lead them into a perpetual state of denial, and they persuade themselves that there is absolutely nothing wrong whilst everyone else around them clearly knows there is. They are hoping, of course, that their problems will somehow just go away and be forgotten. It is like the woman who discovers a breast lump and is afraid that the doctor may diagnose a malignancy, so she refuses to make an appointment and completely ignores it.

Dangerous Stress Defence Mechanisms

Denial is just one example of some of the dangerous and inappropriate defence mechanisms which people use when they are under stress. There are many others, and most of us will recognise some of these common traits.

1. Blaming Others

By deliberately choosing not to examine our own behaviour and attitudes, any faults and inconsistencies in our thought processes and conduct can be overlooked. People who disassociate in this way are very good at blaming others when in fact their own weaknesses and faults are considerable. Bosses who do this at work create huge problems for their staff, and people who do it at home undermine otherwise healthy relationships.

2. Taking It Out on Someone Else

Here the person under undue stress displaces his emotions from an appropriate source to an inappropriate source. Most of us have been guilty of it at some time, for example biting our tongue when we are furious with our colleagues at work and then coming home and taking it out on the family or the cat.

3. Making Excuses for Your Own Bad Behaviour

In psychological terms it is called 'rationalisation' and is used to describe a kind of self-deception where seemingly socially acceptable reasons are found for doing something which actually has a less worthy motive. Doing something dishonourable 'to teach someone else a lesson' would be a good example.

4. Over-Compensating When Insecure

Mr Brittas of TV's popular sitcom *The Brittas Empire* was a caricature of the over-compensating individual. He typifies the person who behaves in such a way as to camouflage a weakness or a sense of inferiority. By going too far, he exhibits a veneer of power and authority which belies the insecurity beneath the surface.

5. Translating Fear into Illness

Someone with underlying fears can convert these anxieties into various types of physical symptoms. For example, a child being bullied at school will turn up with a tummy ache just after breakfast as a way of avoiding having to go to school. An adult who is dreading a confrontation with a superior at work may become housebound with a migraine or a backache.

6. Retiring into a Shell

Excessively stressed individuals who can see no way out of their situation retire from it physically and emotionally, and simply give up. They lose their interest and enthusiasm, find concentration and motivation difficult, and become apathetic and depressed.

These are all examples of unhelpful defence mechanisms which most of us use from time to time. But if we are going to be able to deal with stress effectively we have to acknowledge these negative tendencies and discover other more appropriate methods of handling stress. Unless we can find and practice these other methods, we are likely to go on harming ourselves in unhelpful ways or resorting to even worse behavioural symptoms such as escapist drinking and other forms of substance abuse.

Even Worse Stress Behavioural Symptoms

Taking Drugs

When people are under pressure you often see them reaching for a cigarette. Alternatively they might come storming in through the front door at home saying, 'God, I need a drink!' Others might take even more addictive types of recreational drugs and some, who have got as far as seeing their GP, may even resort to swallowing excessive amounts of the medicines originally prescribed to alleviate their symptoms, such as Valium or Librium. All of these substances are false friends because they lull us into a false sense of security, a kind of temporary relief from life's various pressures. This makes successful stress adaptation mechanisms much more difficult to achieve. The two commonest emotional props of all, of course, are smoking and alcohol.

Smoking
Although more and more people are managing to give up smoking, the commonest reason for failing to do so is exposure to continual stress. Most people have already taken on board the messages about smoking and cancer, or smoking and heart disease. When people are continually stressed, however, dealing with those unpleasant symptoms is their first priority and they are unable to think about long-term damage to their well-being. For them, the cigarette is a prop, a little pleasure in a sea of problems, and to give up would be a tremendous sacrifice. Unfortunately, nicotine is one of the most addictive drugs known to man. The nicotine which circulates in the bloodstream soon after inhaling the first couple of puffs results in a feeling of relaxation and confidence. But the nervous system soon gets used to the effects of regular smoking, and a restless sensation, a feeling of something being missing, is experienced. It is only offset by the next cigarette and so the vicious circle is established. Since stressful situations encourage us to smoke, stressful situations are instrumental in getting us hooked. Giving up smoking becomes stressful in itself, and we will have done our health considerable harm in the process. Better not to start smoking at all or, once we have, to recognise that no difficult situation in life was ever made better in the long term by smoking. Our

addiction to nicotine is only adding new problems for the future. If you really want to give up, try following the simple measures described below.

IF YOU REALLY WANT TO GIVE UP SMOKING

1. Decide to give up once and for all and choose a special day to start. Tell yourself that you really can achieve your ambition and that only by making a real commitment to it will you succeed.

2. Remember that although it will be hard at first to overcome the craving for a cigarette, the addiction soon fades and within a month your body has got rid of almost all traces of the nicotine which has done so much damage. So hang in there!

3. Keep reminding yourself of all the good reasons why you are giving up smoking. You know about the pleasure you got from smoking, but don't allow yourself to dwell on this. Focus only on the benefits you are going to attain from giving up.

4. Do not cut down gradually as this is a constant temptation to smoke more, and an unnecessary form of self-torture. Most smokers who successfully manage to quit do so in one fell swoop.

5. Avoid going to places and getting into situations where you are more likely to smoke. Avoid pubs and restaurants, and friends who smoke and who may well try to encourage you to take up smoking again in order to feel reassured themselves.

6. Praise yourself on the wisdom of what you are doing, the will-power that you are exercising, and all the positive gains that you will make in the future. You can certainly do it if you try.

Alcohol

If alcohol was a true friend of the stressed and oppressed it would not account for so many broken marriages, wrecked family lives, disastrous careers and ill-health. Just like cigarette smoking, its initial use in moderation is a sociable and pleasurable experience but it is incredibly easy to abuse. Many lifestyles and occupations encourage heavy drinking, but poor nutrition, fatigue and stress, as well as a person's basic genetic make-up, can all lead to a dependence on alcohol. Warning signs of this include needing a drink on a regular basis in order to feel all right, and developing a routine of drinking every day. Drinking may even become almost a pastime in its own right, taking precedence over other hobbies, interests and activities. Someone who is drinking too much becomes tolerant to the effects of alcohol and finds themselves having to drink more and more to achieve the effect they desire. When they stop drinking they develop withdrawal symptoms such as nausea, headache, shaking, sweating and restlessness. They then drink more to get rid of these unpleasant withdrawal symptoms and eventually start drinking secretly and running into social problems – drink driving, missing the last train home, making frequent mistakes at work, or becoming violent and aggressive. Current recommendations for sensible limits for drinking are up to twenty-eight units a week for men and twenty-one units a week for women, although it must be pointed out that this amount is not compulsory! The limits are there to warn people that drinking more than this number of units over seven days will be associated with an increased risk of social, psychological and physical symptoms in the long term. A man drinking more than fifty-six units a week or a woman drinking more than thirty-five units a week is at very great risk of running into severe alcohol-related difficulties.

A unit of alcohol is the equivalent of:

- half a pint of beer or normal strength cider;
- a single pub measure of spirits or fortified wine (sherry, apéritif etc.); or
- a small glass of wine.

The side-effects of alcohol dependence are just as bad for the lonely, isolated housewife as they are for the busy executive or manager. After the first couple of units the average drinker is feeling fine and in control but, despite being unaware of it, their ability to work and to react quickly is hampered. As they drink more they start to lose control and judgement, making mistakes and becoming more prone to accidents. Further drinking produces problems with physical co-ordination. The person becomes uninhibited, sometimes embarrassingly so, and is now beyond the legal limit for driving. Drinking even more results in obvious physical clumsiness, slurred speech and slow thought processes. If the person keeps on drinking, they will gradually lose consciousness. The initial prop that was used to alleviate stress has become a source of stress in itself, and a hugely destructive one at that. There are some simple tips below to help you cut down.

IF YOU WANT TO CUT DOWN YOUR DRINKING

1. Keep a drink diary and tot up your total number of alcohol units consumed in a week on a day-to-day basis. Try to identify in your diary the times and situations where you are most likely to drink, and then avoid them.
2. Reduce your weekly amount by cutting out drinking at certain times, for example lunch time and go to the gym, have a decent meal or go for a walk instead.
3. When you drink, drink only one unit an hour and have a glass of water for every alcohol unit you drink.
4. Drink spritzers or low-alcohol drinks to increase the volume and help slow down consumption.
5. Draw up a plan to get out of drinking, especially drinking in 'rounds' when these situations arise.
6. Remember all the benefits to cutting down on booze. It will be easier to lose weight as alcohol is so high in calories and your mental agility, general well-being and good health will soon improve. You will feel more motivated to adopt a healthy lifestyle generally.

Other Harmful Stress Props

There are many other substances which people use to try to escape from the effects of unpleasant stress. These include excess consumption of caffeine in tea, coffee and cola drinks and all of the recreational 'designer' drugs, such as cocaine, speed, crack and ecstasy. Medicinal drugs may also be abused, either by obtaining them on the black market or as a result of the doctor overprescribing. Whatever the substance of abuse however, stress cannot be alleviated in this way. It can only become more intense as a result. You can certainly run from stress but it will always catch up with you in the end. You can run but you still can't hide. Eventually you have to deal with it in a more appropriate and effective way. The following chapters tell you how.

CHAPTER TWELVE

GETTING WHAT YOU WANT FROM LIFE

Very few people are entirely content with every aspect of their lives. How many of us, I wonder, really get what we want, or say we want, from life? How many of us ever really stop to think what that might be? Many symptoms of stress stem from unresolved and subconscious mental conflict or a nagging feeling of restlessness and self-doubt, a sense of being out of control of our own destiny. How many people say to themselves, 'I feel everything is getting on top of me, but I don't know why?' How many people wonder where it's all going to end, what it's all about and what the purpose of it all is? The reason they feel like this is because they have never worked out these answers for themselves, and have no specific direction or purpose. They go with the tide and end up wherever life happens to take them. They believe in the philosophy that when one door shuts another door opens. They are happy to wait and see what happens and what will be around the next corner without ever looking at a map and questioning whether they want to go there or not. The trouble with this dependence on destiny and on other people's initiatives is that it never allows you to take control and so you become exposed to unwelcome events as well as welcome ones. In fact, the majority of people never do decide upon a clear long-term objective. Very few people actively pursue an aim or goal except, that is, the more successful individuals in our midst. These people, and the profitable and booming organisations for which they work, always seem to have an objective and a plan.

What Do You Want From Life?

When you have worked out a life plan of sorts, it really helps you to put things in perspective, to manage your time better, and to work with motivation and direction. It is possible to look at a life plan and set yourself priorities so that you are less likely to become distracted by unimportant events. Try assessing your current situation by asking yourself the following questions.

1. What do you regret not having achieved so far in your life?

A common source of stress in many middle-aged men and women stems from unfulfilled ambition. There may have been a number of things you wanted to achieve by a certain age but, one way or another, it never quite happened. You may have noticed other people – subordinates, juniors and younger members of staff – forging ahead and actually reaching the targets that you once set yourself but only in a rather vague sort of way.

2. What are your hopes and aspirations, and what are you good at?

Where do your natural talents and skills lie? If you drifted into a job or, have become disillusioned with it because the nature of the job changed around you and you never adapted, it may well be that you are not using all your skills to the best of your ability because you have never really pushed yourself.

3. If you had more free time, how would you spend it?
Which hobbies and interests give you the most pleasure?
Would you like to spend time on reading, or learning new
skills like learning to play a musical instrument or painting? Or
would you like to spend more time with the family, or just
seeing friends?

**4. Last time you had a long break or a holiday, what sort
of things did you find yourself thinking about for the
future?**
At relaxing times like this you get one of the rare opportunities in life to actually stop and think about those objectives.

People generally avoid setting themselves targets because they
too easily become distracted by less important things along
the way or because the ambitions they choose for themselves
are too ambitious and unrealistic. But they also underestimate
their abilities. They imagine setting themselves a goal and
working towards it, but then failing to achieve it and getting
depressed and fed up. If you think hard about the questions
above and your answers to them, most of what you want to do
in life is actually achievable. This is where some kind of life
plan, setting out your objectives, can come in useful. With just
a few relatively minor changes anything is possible.

How to Work Out a Life Plan

Use the list below to formulate your thoughts. Give yourself
adequate time to think about each category and then write
everything down. Remember to put in even those ambitions
which you previously thought would be impossible to
achieve.

Your Job
- What type of work would you like to do?
- What type of company would you like to work for?
- What position in that company would you like to reach?

Your Salary
- What realistic figure would you like to achieve?

Your Private Life
- Where do you see you and your family in the years to come?

Your Friends
- Do you want to spend more time with them?
- Who are the people you have never met but would like to?
- Do you fancy doing any voluntary work?
- Would it be useful to get to know your neighbours better?

Your Physical Fitness
- Are you as fit as you'd like to be?
- Do you want to be more involved in sport, either as a participant or as a spectator?

Your Psychological Well-being
- Do you want to learn new skills?
- Do you want to learn a new language?
- Do you want to be given more responsibility?
- Do you want to explore spiritual or healing disciplines?

Time to Yourself
- Do you get enough time on your own?
- Are you able to relax?
- Are you happy with your style and appearance?

Your Possessions

- Do you want to do anything about your car?
- Do you want to move house?
- Is there anything else you really want?

Your Interests

- Would you like to travel more?
- Would you like to take more holidays?
- Do you spend enough time on the hobbies you used to enjoy?
- Are you able to escape the city and wander around the countryside?
- Do you get a chance to learn new skills?

Go back through the list and add other categories if you wish. Against each suggestion put an 'L' for 'Like to Do' or an 'M' for 'Must Do'. This gives you some idea of priority. Then go back again and set yourself a realistic time period in which to achieve it. Now concentrate on how you are going to be able to achieve the things you want in life, and spend time and effort accordingly on them. Look at your life plan regularly every month and then draw up a modified list of objectives and plans each year. Finally, just imagine how you would feel if you achieved everything on your list. It would be tremendous wouldn't it? The truth is, that with a little effort of will, and better planning and prioritising, you actually can achieve it. One of the first things you will need to do is to remove any unnecessary pressure from the sources that are really getting in your way. But there is plenty you can do yourself to ease these pressures.

CHAPTER THIRTEEN

WHAT YOU CAN DO TO
EASE THE PRESSURE

As we saw in Chapter 2 staying in control, and using healthy levels of stress to our advantage, is all about achieving the right balance between the pressures we face in life and the coping mechanisms with which we handle them. When either one is outweighed by the other, we experience those unpleasant symptoms and signs of stress which can seriously reduce the quality of our lives.

Once you have learned to familiarise yourself with the warning signs of excessive stress, you can do something about it. You know that it will ultimately affect you or your health and the way you lead your life, so you know it is vital that you should do something about it. Having read the earlier chapters in this book, you should also be able to recognise your own personal sources of stress. This means that you are now ready to learn how you can step in and actively manage your stress levels more effectively, rather than passively sitting back and letting stress get the better of you. Going back to the example of the tightrope walker in Chapter 2, we saw how we can move from a situation of imbalance and threatened disaster to one of balance and satisfaction, once we have gained control over our lives. If we wish to walk that tightrope successively every day and step off the far side of it smiling, then we have to move from a position where the demands made on us are not balanced by our coping skills to one where the demands are completely balanced by our coping skills.

Tot up Life Events and Stresses

There are a number of things we can do to reduce pressure on ourselves. The first thing we can do is to add up all of the current stresses that exist in our life at the present time, following the simple steps outlined below.

1. Make a list of all of your various sources of stress and how persistent they have been.

2. Arrange your list under various headings, such as 'trivial' and 'serious', remembering that lots of little irritations and niggles can be more upsetting than one single major difficulty.

3. Sort your list out again into the stresses that have immediate practical solutions, those that will get better in their own time, and those that you simply cannot change no matter what you do.

4. Try to stop worrying about the stresses that do not have an obvious practical solution.

5. Start working on the stresses you feel can be changed. It is worth trying possible solutions out, and see how you get on.

Tackling sources of stress may mean upsetting other people, but quite possibly you have been putting yourself out for others for far too long, and now it is time to put yourself first. As regards the other problems, why worry if they are beyond your control? If you are worried, for example, that your teenage son has set his heart on a round-the-world back-packing trek at the potential cost of his place at university, that is surely something that he should be worried about rather than you. If this is truly what he wishes to do, you know that no amount of argument from you is likely to thwart his ambition and it will almost certainly turn out well in the end. You can certainly encourage him to finance the expedition himself in order to motivate him and make him more self-reliant. It could be seen as a positive sign of his maturity and development, and it may be a very good idea to postpone his university course for a year. If you have been feeling tense because of the council digging up the road outside your house, the children refusing to eat 'normal' food, and your holiday plans being cancelled at the last minute, tell yourself that the road will be finished in due course the children will not starve to death, and an alternative holiday will be arranged. Why worry just for the sake of worrying?

Write Things Down

Writing down the various things that are causing you problems can be therapeutic in that it seems to take the problems out of your head and transfer them to the piece of paper instead. This is a great trick for people who cannot sleep as a result of tossing and turning caused by racing thoughts. It is also worth keeping a stress diary for a week or two in which you can note everything that irritates or upsets you. Your diary may look something like the example on the next page.

Day: **Date:**

Possible Sources of Stress	Coping Skill or Goal
	Assessment:

Daily stress diary

By looking back over your diary it may be possible to identify situations, circumstances or people who wind you up, so that you can adopt strategies for avoiding or dealing with the resultant stress in the future. As far as the major life events are concerned, there is clearly nothing you can do about many of them, such as bereavement or physical illness. Everybody has to move house from time to time, divorce and separation are almost epidemic, threat of redundancy is ever present and even the pleasant things in life, like having children, going on holiday, and Christmas, can be immensely stressful. Too many of these events in a short period of time can overwhelm your ability to cope with them, so it is a good idea to tot up the number of life events you have been subject to in the last year and look at your score. Use the list from the Holmes and Rahe Rating Scale on page 71. Since it is known that a score of more than 150 increases your risk of illness during the next two years by fifty percent or more, it is sensible not to take on any more work than you need to. Even though you may not be aware of it, the subconscious strain involved in taking on even small extra tasks does take its toll. So concentrate on dealing with what you have on your plate at present before embarking on new projects and ambitions.

Become Better Organised

Even the most disorganised and happy-go-lucky personalities amongst us have to plan for the future to some extent. They may appear to live for today but most of them know where they are going to sleep each night, where the next meal is coming from, and how much money they will have in their pocket next week. Other people have everything organised down to the very last detail. Not just from day to day, but from hour to hour and minute to minute as well. Both philosophies can in fact engender excessive stress. The trick is to be aware of what is important for you so that you can achieve your targets and get what you want out of life. This means being able to prioritise and be realistic about what is possible.

Draw Up A Life Plan

Drawing up some sort of life plan, as described in the previous chapter, is an extremely useful exercise in giving your life direction and purpose. It is important not to be too ambitious as this will only over burden you with too many self-inflicted demands. Getting a promotion you have been chasing for so long, only to find the job is much harder than you ever dreamed of, would be a major source of stress for you. So look at your life plan again. Look at your priorities, the things you would like to do and the things you must do. Set yourself some kind of a time scale, short term and long term, and then delete the objectives which are frankly unattainable. By being realistic in this way, the sense of achievement and satisfaction when you succeed will be immense. Your self-esteem and confidence will grow and you will then be able to go on to the next level. By over reaching yourself the opposite can occur, you will lose your confidence, feel like a failure and achieve very little.

Be Optimistic and Think Positively

Having a positive outlook means viewing the world with optimistic and hopeful beliefs, expectations and attitudes, rather than seeing as hopeless, futile and gloomy, and pessimistically expecting the worst to happen. Unhelpful thoughts can really hold us back. Take for example the after-dinner speaker. Instead of saying to himself, 'I've prepared a great speech, I know they'll like it and I am going to enjoy giving it', he becomes preoccupied with thoughts of failure. The audience want him to succeed, they want to be entertained, but instead of concentrating on his delivery, a little voice inside his head is asking him if his voice is faltering. Do all these people think he is a bit of a fool? Are his jokes working? These kind of self-doubts and self-criticisms despite adequate preparation may well mean that his speech will not be well received. They can make all the difference between success and failure. The same applies to taking an examination or having a job interview. Thinking, 'I wish this was over and done with,' or 'They think I'm a complete wally,' is unhelpful. More positive, confident thoughts would be more appropriate such as, 'I'm nervous, but that is to be expected and I can handle it,' or, 'These are the main points, and these are the things I want to highlight.'

Change the Way You Think About Things

You can learn to recognise unhelpful ways of thinking, just as you can learn to recognise the signs of stress and then substitute a much more positive approach. Try following the steps below.

1. Start by counting up how many negative and unhelpful thoughts you have every day and how much of the day was taken up with these.

2. Work out several more positive responses that you could have substituted for each unhelpful thought, so that you are seeing each problem in a different light.

3. Practise the positive thoughts and use them for each similar situation in the future.

4. In any given situation, ask yourself whether your thoughts relate to the facts. If you say to yourself, 'I've done hopelessly in that exam' ask yourself if that is really true. What you are probably saying is that you could have done slightly better, but all of us tend to be highly self-critical in that situation. The truth is that all of us can do better at any task and none of us can achieve perfection all the time. You have done the exam and you have done your best, so congratulate yourself on what you have achieved. If you are able to look at alternative interpretations of your negative thoughts in this way and see how damaging it is to blame yourself, you can train yourself to think more positively and feel better about yourself in the process. Thinking positively

gives you a sense of control in your life, of achievement and satisfaction. It motivates you, helps you concentrate, and is picked up by people around you. So remember the following points whenever you are tempted to think negatively.

- Your unhelpful thoughts are not borne out by the true facts.
- You are jumping to conclusions.
- There are other ways of looking at any situation. There is a good side to most things.
- Your unhelpful thoughts may hinder you rather than help you.
- It is unrealistic to think only in terms of black and white.
- Just because one thing goes wrong, it doesn't change everything else.
- You have strengths as well as weaknesses.
- Praise rather than blame yourself.
- You should not shoulder all the responsibility when things go wrong.
- Perfection is rare.
- It is easy to get things out of proportion.
- Trivial problems are never disasters.

Always look for alternatives to unhelpful thinking. Remember that negative thoughts are a barrier to success and healthy self-esteem.

Be More Assertive – Be Able to Say No

Some people find it hard to say no when family, friends or workmates ask a favour of them. They naturally want to be co-operative and helpful and will generally find themselves saying yes, even though they may be snowed under with work already. They put themselves under unnecessary stress by doing so. Often these 'put upon' people are keen to say yes because they need to feel liked and be popular. Occasionally it is because they feel they will not get anywhere in their relationships with others or with promotion at work if they refuse and are perceived to be 'difficult'. But taking on too much in this way increases pressure and reduces performance. Such people often find themselves doing things for other people rather than themselves, perhaps sacrificing the needs of their own family and friends in the process. By becoming more assertive and learning to say no politely, clearly and honestly it is possible to say no without giving offence and without the people who are making these requests disliking you. Often it simply means suggesting alternatives or solutions which are practical for everybody. A good example might be a work situation where a colleague asks you to bale them out of a difficult situation but which involves you in being dishonest, thereby increasing your own stress level. Let's suppose that a colleague tells you they need two or three days off work but are anxious not to have to ask the boss for permission themselves. They ask if you would be willing to tell the boss that their grandmother has died and they have gone off suddenly to sort out the necessary arrangements. You know the person well and this is the first time they have ever put you in this position. You want them to like you, and your first thought is that if you say no you will be letting them down. At the same time, however, you would be exposing yourself to unnecessary stress and to potential difficulties for yourself at work. In short, you would be lying.

A more assertive approach would be to say nicely but firmly that you are unable to say anything which you know to be a lie, and you would be reluctant to do so anyway as this might ultimately get the person concerned into serious trouble if they were found out. You might go on to suggest that they discussed with the boss some days off at short notice out of their holiday allowance or that they approach their family doctor if the reason for wanting time off was due to any ill-effects of stress. In this way you are saying no and protecting yourself, but still helping your colleague at the same time. It is not always easy to turn people down in this way, particularly if you are by nature an easygoing, soft person. But by practising being assertive it will become easier and easier to avoid taking on things which are unpleasant and difficult when you already have enough on your plate as it is. In meetings at work, and in negotiations generally, being assertive is about communicating clearly with other people without there being any mis-understanding. It means coming away from a confrontation knowing that neither party feels resentful or let down. It is nothing to do with aggression, which usually means raised voices, nasty personal remarks and emotional blackmail. Whenever you feel you are being asked something you do not want to do, remember these basic points.

- It is your basic right to say no.
- It is your right to express both positive and negative emotions about something.
- It is your right not to have to get involved with somebody else's problems.
- You should take time to think about the issues before deciding on what to do.
- When you say no, you should say it firmly and clearly so as not to show doubt and invite further pressure.
- Give reasons, not excuses, for your decision.
- Do not waiver.
- Always put forward alternative suggestions and answers.

Work Efficiently

Whether you are working on personal tasks or for your employer, there is nothing worse than being aware of a huge number of tasks which need doing with too little time in which to do them. This is anxiety-provoking and is much more stressful than it need be. However, there are some basic steps you can take.

1. Set down all the jobs you have to do on a piece of paper.

2. Go through them all giving them a planned order of completion based on their level of priority. Give them a score from nought to ten if you find this helpful.

3. Work out which jobs have to be done today, which can be postponed until tomorrow, and which can be done at some time in the future.

4. Ask yourself which jobs are urgent and which jobs are important.

Remember that few jobs are both urgent and important although these will easily command top priority on your list of things to do. Urgent tasks only assume importance because they sometimes appear to warrant immediate action. The trouble is, like an unscheduled telephone interruption, they hold you back from tackling more important but less urgent jobs when they crop up. Try to develop an ability to judge whether tasks are important or urgent so that you can decide whether you need to postpone them or tackle them straight away.

Once you have got your priorities sorted out, deal with the most important tasks first, the ones for which the deadlines are the tightest, and simply refuse to be waylaid by more minor tasks. If some have equal status, deal with the ones which are the most unpleasant first, as the perceived stress of continually postponing them is worse that actually doing them. Remember also to give a high priority to personal and domestic problems. Ignoring them will give rise to concern and anxiety, and your work will only suffer as a result. If any one job appears to be monumental and the workload intense, just try to break it down into small components. Look at each small step at a time rather than the whole mountain ahead of you, and aim to tackle it bit by bit. Finally, do not promise to have the job completed by tomorrow week if doing it by tomorrow week is going to involve working twenty-four hours a day. If you think you can realistically do the job by tomorrow week tell the person concerned that it will be completed in twelve days, thereby giving yourself enough time to review what you do and to improve it in the process, without turning grey overnight.

Delegate to Others

When the pressure on you becomes too great, it is essential to delegate. At home this often means dividing up the household chores more equally, getting your partner and any children to do their share of the load. The old adage 'if you want a job done well, it's best to do it yourself' is really the last resort of the perfectionist who is either stupid enough or arrogant enough to believe that nobody else can be trusted. In reality, this is just not true. Most people are very happy to sit back and watch others do the work by feigning an attitude of 'learned helplessness'. If they were ever in a position where they had to do the chores them-selves, not only would they do them but they would do them quite well. So look at your own workload and share it out with other people. Bear in mind the following tips.

- Try to choose the person who is best suited for any task and who also has enough time to take it on.
- Be sure to give them a clear idea of what you expect of them.
- Make sure you give them all the information they need, but do not be tempted to interfere with the way they are doing it as they need the responsibility and your trust in them to succeed.

At work, delegation makes colleagues feel more a part of the organisation and makes them feel useful. They feel better about themselves, and they rise to the opportunity to show what they can do and demonstrate their skills. For working women who juggle multiple roles as mother, cook, shopper, cleaner, as well as employee, delegating both domestic duties and work is an essential means to survival.

Find Time for Everything

How many times have you recently said 'I'm sorry I haven't got time'? You have probably said it frequently both at work and at home but you are certainly not alone. The trouble with not having enough time is that important things get forgotten, deadlines are never reached, and tension and stress result. Think of the guilt and hassle caused by forgetting someone's birthday or an appointment at work. Think of that constant sense of time slipping by, where you are forever checking your watch and looking at the clock. How much time during a busy working week do you get to see and visit friends, to read books, to relax, to play sport, to spend time with your family, to read the newspapers, or just to sit doing nothing other than reflecting on what you achieved last week and what you hope to achieve next week?

Finding a 'special extra hour' each week

Finding time to enjoy your life is a vital element in stress busting. Getting work done in the time available results from establishing priorities and being realistic about your goals, as we have already seen. Look at the illustration above and imagine that you had an extra hour each week. How would you spend that hour if you could do whatever you wanted with it and could have it whenever you wanted? Make a note of half a dozen things that would make you really content during that hour. Then write down half a dozen things that would make other people happy as a result of what you did. Finally, list half a dozen things which you have been putting off for ages which you could at least make a start on during the sixty minutes. Now look back over the last week to see where this hour could be fitted in. Having found it, fit this stress-busting hour into that place every week in future. Once it becomes a habit you'll find that you are saying 'I just don't have the time' much less often than you used to.

Look at Problems in a Different Way

By replacing negative thoughts with more positive ones, problems can be turned into opportunities. It is very easy to become despondent and demoralised when faced with unexpected problems or snags, but try viewing the next problem as a challenge.

One of my patients who was a natural worrier and something of a hypochondriac had a cervical smear. I was horrified to receive the results from the cytology laboratory informing me that she had cancer of the cervix and would therefore require major gynaecological surgery as a life-saving measure. I dreaded having to break this bad news to her as she was clearly going to find it difficult, if not impossible, to deal with the implications. We both invested a lot of time and care in talking this problem through and identifying ways of dealing with it. So successful was the result that not only did she come through a successful operation with flying colours and a clean bill of health ten years later, but she also went on to organise a local fund-raising organisation for a cervical cancer charity in the area. She became a confident and effective public speaker for the benefit of hundreds of other women faced with similar problems.

Another example of turning problems into opportunities comes from the McDonald's burger chain. A disillusioned salesman called Ray Kroc had been thwarted in his ambitions of starting a fast-food restaurant and had failed to make a killing in the milkshake mixer trade. One day he called in at a restaurant which needed eight of his mixers. He was impressed by the set-up of the restaurant as it matched his own thoughts and ideas on what would succeed as a rapidly expanding business. He could have thought 'I've been beaten to it, I might as well give up' but he was more positive. Instead, he negotiated the right to franchise the McDonald name throughout the world and became extremely successful as a result.

Help Yourself

In all of these methods of reducing pressures on yourself, you are never alone. There are friends, relatives, family and colleagues with whom to share your difficulties, and who are able to support you. It obviously helps to be in the right job and if you are not, or have ambitions elsewhere, then look again at your life plan and give yourself a timescale for finding the correct one. If you are a perfectionist, ask yourself whether you are really achieving more than you would if you just did jobs reasonably well or to a high average standard. Going for the extra ten percent is hardly ever noticed by other people and is achieved only at enormous cost to yourself and to other tasks.

Another simple trick in reducing your perceived workload is to ask for help when it is needed. Pride in your work and not wanting to ask other people are admirable qualities, but working every waking hour ineffectively and at enormous cost to your health and happiness is plain crazy. If you are being given too much to do, you need to discuss it with your boss and if you are being asked to do the wrong things, this needs sorting out as well. Sharing problems with friends and colleagues means halving problems, and it is highly reassuring to know that others are often suffering from the same kind of tensions and stresses.

Try Working to Live Rather Than Living to Work

If you find yourself staying behind after work to do things which could be done tomorrow, or if you are taking work home at the end of the day and constantly talking about work with friends and family, you should ask yourself why. If you are having to rearrange your holiday around important meetings or events at work, if you are constantly seeking promotion, constantly questioning how you are getting on, the same question arises. You may have slipped into workaholic mode, something that, can happen insidiously. Look again at the life plan which you have drawn up. What about the items outside work, like spending time with family and friends, taking on new hobbies and learning new skills, or simply relaxing? Think once again about your objectives in life, and about setting yourself realistic targets with realistic timescales in which to achieve them.

Reduce the Stress of Boredom

When our talents are underused and we feel bored and frustrated, our self-esteem plummets, our motivation flies out of the window, and we perform badly. This is a situation common to people facing retirement as well as redundancy, and it is every bit as stressful to have too little demands made upon us as it is to have too many. In health terms it has been shown in medical studies that the perceived stress in assembly line workers doing forty hours a week was actually much greater than in general practitioners whose work was varied, challenging and highly responsible but who were working much longer hours. In fact, it is worth remembering that probably the only source of stress which is greater than having too much work is the stress of unemployment.

Other people who experience the purposelessness and emptiness of not having enough to do are people who have recently been bereaved, or parents whose children have grown up and recently left home. They have the ability to cope with far more demands than are currently made of them, and should seek out new challenges such as:

- travelling;
- learning new skills;
- taking on fresh training;
- attending evening classes;
- enjoying sport;
- embarking on a new hobby or pastime and
- joining voluntary organisations and taking part in community projects.

Any of these activities can be therapeutic. In any of these ways all of us are able to reduce the pressures upon us and do something actively to make life not only more bearable but more pleasurable too.

CHAPTER FOURTEEN

BECOMING A CALMER PERSON

Some people are 'born' stressed, some people acquire stress and others have stress thrust upon them. Those who inherit the stressed-out personality exhibit Type A behaviour, which was explained in Chapter 5.

The problem is that Type A behaviour is neither healthy nor productive. All the evidence suggests that Type A individuals are more likely to have serious illnesses, like heart attacks and strokes, and that despite working excessive hours, they ultimately achieve little more than others whose working patterns are more balanced. But even people who are inherently stressed can learn to alter their beliefs, attitudes and habits in order to enjoy a better quality and quantity of life. There is little point in becoming easily upset or angry over trivial things. There is nothing at all to be gained from coming home frustrated and ranting and raving at your partner and the children. Furthermore, strong scientific research shows that even after somebody has had a heart attack, they can reduce the chances of a second attack by fifty percent or more, if they modify their habits.

However, it means making a commitment to changing. It means finding time to stop and consider what you want from your life, what you are achieving now as a result of your Type A behaviour, and what can still be achieved through modifying it. Embarking on fundamental change often only comes about when some ghastly disaster has already befallen the victim. It might be a heart attack, or it could be a divorce or separation resulting from your previous attitude and lifestyle. It could be a nervous breakdown or even the experience of being caught up in a completely spontaneous but extremely violent road-rage episode. Events like these are sufficient to make even the most driven and manic Type A individual stop and take notice. These are amongst the few opportunities and occasions in our lives when we can actually ask ourselves, 'Is it all worth it? Do the ends really justify the means? Was this what I set out to do all those years ago? What has been the cost of me going down this road? What the hell am I doing it for?'

There is a certain proud, rather arrogant but repressed Type A individual whom I occasionally encounter in my surgery. They obviously think coming to see me is a sign of weakness since they apologise for being there and wasting my time. They frequently throw in the comment that they would not have come had it not been for their partner pestering them to do so. But then, as we talk over the way they lead their life and what is happening to them and to their family, they are sometimes able to acknowledge the appalling toll that their attitudes and beliefs have had on their daily existence, their health and their social life. Sometimes the advice I give goes straight in one ear and out of the other. It is advice which the patient really does not wish to hear. As a result, the vicious circle continues until an even worse crisis or disaster befalls them. Alternatively, if the person concerned will accept a short-term sick note on either physical or psychological grounds, they can spend a few days mulling over things. They need to make a firm commitment to take stock of their life so far and to alter their behaviour in the future so that the rest of it can be enjoyed.

How to Modify Type A Behaviour

Behaviour modification involves learning about oneself and then practising drills to change from being a stressed-out individual to a calmer one. It takes time and practice but is well worth doing. To become a calmer person you need to adopt the following behaviour patterns.

Stop rushing about everywhere
Stop living by the clock, and slow down. There are only 168 hours in every week and this figure will never change. It is also exactly the same length of week for everybody else, and since they all manage to do the jobs required in the time available, there is no reason why you cannot.

Concentrate on finishing one job at a time
Try to enjoy each job in the process. Type A individuals tend to juggle several jobs at once, while doing none of them terribly effectively. They even read their notes in the car whilst driving to work in the morning, or take work into the toilet with them so as not to 'waste time'.

Learn to wait patiently when you have to
Make constructive use of your time whilst waiting. Save all that wasteful energy that is taken up in tapping your foot, wringing your hands, pulling your hair or biting your nails. If you really have to wait then read a newspaper or a book, and use the time for a worthwhile purpose so as not to become tense and anxious.

Try and avoid situations which you find particularly irritating
If it is the heavy traffic in the rush hour that bothers you most, try getting up an hour earlier to beat the rush hour and use the time at the other end to take some regular exercise. Or even start work early and finish early, if you can negotiate working flexi-time.

Do not set yourself unnecessary deadlines
Avoid filling your diary with back-to-back appointments. Many people suffering from stress bring pressures upon themselves by making unrealistic and unnecessary promises about when they can deliver work or complete jobs. Booking back-to-back appointments leaves no time for unforeseen extensions or interruptions, and no time whatsoever for breaks, social time or relaxation. Include in your diary appointments for social and idling time. Cross off gaps between appointments to allow time to take stock of things and put your feet up for a few minutes. You will work better and more efficiently by doing so.

Stop getting angry about things over which you have no control
There will always be somebody at work who winds you up, and situations in which you automatically become embroiled, but avoid the hook that pulls you in to these circumstances. Just take a few deep breaths, resist the temptation to jump in, and tell yourself that it really does not matter. You cannot always exert your will over everybody else's and there are some things you just will never be able to change. Accept them and let the moment pass. Anger and hostility are really just manifestations of your own low self-esteem. By thinking positive thoughts and being assertive, you can rise above it all yet still feel in control. This means that you have to accept the

mistakes and stupidities of other people as well as acknowledging your own faults. Everybody makes mistakes, and the world would be a boring place if everybody was exactly the same, but you do not need to suffer fools gladly, just suffer fools occasionally.

Try to be a good listener

People who are highly stressed have a habit of nodding energetically when other people are talking to them and turning sideways on, as if they are ready to go before the other person has finished their sentence. These are non-verbal cues for the other person to hurry up, implying that either what they are saying is of no interest or they are being too long-winded. But as the ancient Greek philosopher Zeto of Citium said, 'The reason why we have two ears and only one mouth is that we may listen the more and talk the less.'

It is good to listen, and to practice listening, because it is a considerable skill in itself. You may well have other things on your mind, you might very well rather be elsewhere and you may very well be tired, but even if you have no apparent interest in what the speaker is saying, perhaps you should have. You should not let your own ideas and prejudices cloud your understanding, and if you never listen you will never learn. Apart from anything else, the highly stressed individual may hear what they least want to from true friends or family – that they are becoming a rather unattractive and unpleasant person, and that they have stopped being interested in the things that most people hold dear to them, namely their partner, children, friends and relations.

Learn to relax

Appreciate the environment about you as this is important in improving the quality of life. How often does the driven executive find time to recall fond memories, to observe wildlife or to appreciate beautiful buildings? How often does the workaholic commute to and from work every morning seeing nothing of interest during the entire journey? Learning to relax is a vital opportunity to recharge one's batteries and unwind (see Chapter 15).

Become less competitive

Play games for fun rather than always to win. The frantic workaholic who forces his way up the squash league as a result of sheer effort will always get a drubbing from a better player at some time. There is always a sense of achievement and satisfaction in winning an important match but there is equal satisfaction in having a game with a lesser player, where new and more tricky shots can be practised and mastered, or playing your young son or daughter and teaching them the game for their future enjoyment. You do not always have to win. There is nobody on earth who has always won, not even world champions.

Keep your sense of humour

People who take life too seriously are not much fun and are certainly not very pleasant to work with. Where is the joy if life becomes devoid of little moments of spontaneous fun? It is important to smile, to laugh and give others support and affection. Not only that, but it can provide motivation, inspiration and support to other people. It means you are less likely to blame other people, and it offers you a safety valve for any frustrations and hassles. Laughter truly is the best medicine. To keep that sense of humour, however, you need to spend quality time with the people closest to you. Spend more time with your partner and your children, or why else are you with them and why did you have them? The more time you spend with your family, the more time you will want to spend with them, and the closer your bond will be.

How to Put Your Resolve into Practice

It is all very well setting out to change your behaviour in these ways but it does take time and practice. The best way is to set yourself some drills designed to force you to do the opposite of what you would usually do. There are lots of these you can practise, but start off by making a weekly diary whereby you attempt one every day. You could start off, for example, at the weekend by deliberately choosing the longest queue at the supermarket check-out. As you wait patiently, observe in other people all the impatient characteristic traits which were once present in yourself. You could also leave your watch off so that you are not constantly referring to the clock. One day the following week you could try driving to work using the slow lane only. Another day you could ensure that you have one full hour's lunch break where work is never mentioned. You could deliberately speak or walk more slowly, and so on. Here are some other drills that you can incorporate into your diary over the weeks and months ahead, and which are designed to reduce your sense of time urgency and to decrease your frustration and anger.

- Do everything more slowly.
- Tell your partner and children you love them.
- Do things which show your family you love them.
- Observe the environment around you.
- Consciously avoid physical manifestations of tension, such as gritting your teeth, tapping your foot or clenching your fist.
- Listen to music rather than watching television.

- Be prepared to question whether you are right or not.
- Leave your watch off.
- Take all your allowed breaks at work.
- Practise listening to what other people say.
- Ask a friend or colleague about their health and what is happening in their life.
- Put thirty minutes every day in your diary for yourself.
- Eat more slowly and have social lunches.
- Practise being more assertive.
- Try reading for thirty minutes every day.
- Practise understanding and controlling your anger.
- Spend less time talking about yourself in conversations.
- Look up an old friend or enjoy old memories.
- Take up a new interest.
- Take a different route to work.
- Soak in a relaxing bath for twenty minutes.
- Enjoy a joke every day.
- Write a letter or buy a small gift for someone.
- Practise short relaxation routines.
- Teach your children a new trick.
- Book some time with your partner or give them a surprise.

These are just some of the exercises you can do to start modifying your Type A behaviour. Sit down and plan what you want to do with your 168-hour week, remembering what is most important in your personal life plan. Remind yourself of what you are trying to achieve by leaving notes on your computer screen, on your television at home, on your telephone, or stuck to your watch-face. Recruit help from a trusted and respected friend or a member of the family who can make helpful suggestions when you falter or slip back into old behaviour patterns. Time may be money but time is also precious to you as a person. As the saying goes, 'for every sixty seconds you are angry you lose a minute of happiness'. Make sure that your work is contained to a degree where you enjoy it and achieve your ambition, but where your personal and home life can still flourish and blossom.

Coping With Panic Attacks

Many circumstances or thoughts can trigger off panicky feelings. The anxiety is associated with muscle tension, trembling, butterflies in the stomach, rapid breathing, cold sweats and palpitations. The feeling is certainly unpleasant, but the thing to remember is that it will pass after a little time. First of all, take a deep breath. Then slow down while deepening your breathing pattern. Concentrate on something else to distract yourself from fuelling further panic. As the anxiety diminishes, plan to do something pleasant next. Worrying is a pointless activity which solves nothing. In order to solve your difficulties, you need to work out ways of rethinking them in a more positive manner, and to adopt a more appropriate response. This can be done through a combination of relaxation and professional help when necessary, as we will see in the following chapters.

CHAPTER FIFTEEN

LEARNING THE ART OF RELAXATION

The opposite of the stress response is the relaxation response, which in biological terms is every bit as important. It involves the part of the nervous system which slows our heart beat, regulates our breathing, warms our skin and smoothly controls digestive processes. It brings about sleep and a sense of peace and tranquility. It is a much more passive response than the stress response, however. In a world where human beings are perpetually being put under strain and pressure, we have to work at promoting relaxation by switching off the stress response and allowing the body to rest and restore its natural rhythm.

Relaxation is a skill that everybody should master. It is a vital element in leading a healthy lifestyle, and its benefits are many and varied. Its importance has been recognised for centuries as part of the Eastern philosophies, and nowadays more and more people in the West are beginning to practise relaxation techniques. This includes the conventional medical profession, who are becoming increasingly aware of its advantages to their patients. It is useful in easing muscular tension which brings about headaches and migraine; it helps reduce blood pressure and even blood cholesterol levels; it is of benefit in circulatory disorders where blood flow to the skin is restricted, as in Raynaud's disease. It is also helpful in treating arthritis, irritable bowel syndrome, anxiety states, panic attacks, sleeping disorders and a host of other physical conditions.

Mental well-being is enhanced too. Alertness and concentration can be improved, and memory and creativity may also receive a boost. Above all, relaxation means that people can become less dependent on artificial sedatives such as tranquillizers, anti-depressants and hypnotic drugs. It provides time out from the turmoil and chaos going on around us, a chance for the human body and spirit to recharge its chronically drained batteries.

There are many varied techniques which you can choose to help you relax but whichever you choose, it should be practised on a regular basis in order to gain maximum benefit for your physical and psychological health. Frequent use of a relaxation technique will also make it much easier for you to handle episodes of acutely intense stress, the kind of stress which leads to so many of the unpleasant symptoms and signs which we have all experienced. The relaxation technique you use should be routinely practised whether or not you feel stressed. Only by doing this can the insidious ravages of the ongoing stress response be neutralised.

How to Prepare for Relaxation

1. Find a quiet place where you will not be disturbed by anybody, or by the telephone. Make sure this place is warm and quiet.

2. Sit in a comfortable chair with your feet flat on the floor, relaxing your shoulders and sinking back into the chair which supports you.

3. Slip off your shoes, uncross your legs and rest your arms on your lap.

4. Consciously slow your rate of breathing taking deep, regular breaths.

5. Breathe out for twice as long as you breathe in, controlling the rhythm by silently counting to yourself.

6. Close your eyes and as you continue to breathe rhythmically, clear your mind of all thoughts and worries.

7. Carrying on with the deep breathing, concentrate now on where the muscular tensions are in your body.

8. Stop the deep breathing at any time if you begin to feel dizzy.

9. Breathe in through your nose and out through your mouth, expanding your abdomen as you inhale and raising your rib cage to allow more air to flow in, until your lungs feel completely filled. Then hold your breath for five or six seconds before breathing out again slowly, allowing your rib cage and stomach to relax, emptying your lungs totally.

10. Carry on with the breathing exercise for five minutes or so.

11. You are now ready to start a muscular relaxation technique, but contemplate a while longer if you wish to concentrate on anything which you know will relax you further. Think about fond memories, happy events and wonderful holidays. Concentrate on events that have made you satisfied and fulfilled in the past. This combination of thinking relaxing thoughts and deep slow breathing means that the next step will be even more effective.

Progressive Muscular Relaxation

Having established the regular breathing pattern, you are now ready to start the next procedure. Tense each part of the body as you breathe in. Then hold your breath for five seconds whilst you keep the muscles tense. Relax and breathe out again slowly over a count of about ten seconds.

1. Curl your toes right up and press down with your feet, then relax.

2. Press your heels down pulling your toes up. Relax.

3. Tense your calf muscles. Relax.

4. Straighten your legs and tense your thigh muscles. Relax.

5. Tighten your buttocks. Relax.

6. Tighten your stomach muscles. Relax.

7. Bend your elbows up and flex your biceps. Relax.

8. Hunch your shoulders and tense your neck muscles. Relax.

9. Clench your teeth, frown and screw up your eyes as tight as you can. Relax.

10. Now tense all your muscles at the same time. After ten seconds, relax.

11. Now close your eyes. Concentrate your mind on an imaginary diamond glinting on a black velvet background for thirty seconds as you continue to breathe slowly and deeply.

12. Now focus on another peaceful object of your choice for thirty seconds.

13. Now open your eyes.

This technique is designed to help you recognise muscular tension in your body so that you can learn to relax it at will. The more the technique is practised, the easier it will become. You can do it in the car (when stationary!), in the office, on the bus, practically anywhere. You will not always have the opportunity to sit in a quiet, warm place where there are no disturbances, but there is a short cut that you can take, a sort of shortened form of the relaxation technique called the quieting reflex.

The Quieting Reflex

This is a much shorter routine which only takes a few seconds to do and can help to reverse the activation of the stress response.

1. Close your eyes and identify what it is that is irritating you.

2. Silently say to yourself, 'Sharp mind, relaxed body, I can deal with this.'

3. Smile to yourself inwardly without using any facial muscles. See yourself as a small child and imagine this child on your lap now with your arms around them protecting them.

4. Breathe in slowly to the count of four, imagining the air coming in through the soles of your feet. Imagine a sensation of warmth and goodness gradually filling your body, starting at your feet and welling upwards to your abdomen, chest, then right to the top of your head.

5. Now breathe out to the count of four. Imagine your breath passing downwards from the top of your head and out of the soles of the feet. Feel that warmth and goodness flowing right through you. As you do this, relax your muscles and let your neck, jaw, shoulders and limbs go limp.

6. Open your eyes now and carry on what you were doing before. With practice, the quieting reflex can become so easy and automatic it can enable you to overcome any of those events during the day which make you irritable, frustrated and tense.

Deep Muscular Relaxation

For some people, progressive muscular relaxation is not recommended as tensing the muscles can raise the blood pressure. For those suffering with hypertension, this should be avoided. Instead, deep muscular relaxation can be practised. This is a similar technique, except that the muscles are not deliberately tensed before relaxing. Allow about twenty minutes for this and, if it helps, practise the technique while listening to a relaxation audio tape or to soft tranquil music.

1. Choose a quiet, warm room free from all distractions. Close the curtains and turn off the light.

2. Lie on a comfortable, flat surface with a pillow supporting your head and another under your knees if you wish. Close your eyes. Settle yourself into the most comfortable position you can find, legs slightly apart and hands loosely by your sides.

3. Now focus on the muscles of your abdomen. Feel the tension unwinding and flowing away. Let the small of your back touch the floor and the muscles go completely limp and loose.

4. Breathe slowly and deeply. Let all thoughts leave your mind. Concentrate solely on the music and how weight-less you feel. Relax and feel at peace.

5. Now focus on the muscles of your arms, let them feel heavy yet weightless. Allow them to hang loosely by your sides and feel the tension flow from your fingertips. Relax and breathe slowly and deeply. Feel all of your body completely relax. Breathe slowly and deeply.

6. Now focus on the muscles in your legs. Let them lie completely unsupported on the floor. Allow them to be heavy, dull yet weightless. Be completely aware of the lack of tension in all of your body. Breathe slowly and deeply. Feel calm and relaxed.

7. Now feel how all of your body is completely relaxed. Suspended in weightlessness. Completely relaxed. Breathe slowly and deeply.

8. Allow your breath to leave your lungs completely as you breathe out each time. Allow your chest to collapse and then take a new deep breath.

9. Repeat the process over and over again. Always slowly. Breathe deeply and slowly, relax and savour the sensation. Now you have achieved complete relaxation and are free of all tension. You will feel both relaxed and content.

Meditation

Whereas muscular relaxation concentrates on calming the body physically, meditation relaxes the mind. Meditation has been a central part of many different religions, and has frequently been used as a means of achieving spiritual awareness and fulfilment. For others, however, meditation can be used simply to release inner turmoil and achieve a state of deep relaxation by sweeping all distracting thoughts and worries from the mind. Although a number of different organisations teach meditation, the most commonly practised form in the West is transcendental meditation (TM) where the individual is given a focal device, or mantra, which the meditator says over and over again to himself. The mantra is a personal secret word or sound which should have no emotional meaning whatsoever. The word could be 'om' or 'rah'. Some prefer to use a word with a peaceful connotation such as 'ocean' or 'void'. Having chosen the focal device, follow these steps.

1. Choose a quiet environment and a comfortable position.

2. Take off your shoes and loosen all tight clothing.

3. Consciously let go and be aware of the silence around you as well as the gentle ebb and flow of your breathing.

4. Breathe in and out gently through your nose.

5. As you breathe out say the word 'rah' silently to yourself.

6. Breathe in again gently repeating the word 'rah' as you exhale.

7. Carry on doing this, concentrating only on your breathing and the repetition of the word 'rah'.

8. Clear your mind totally of all distractions. If you find that your mind wanders, or that distracting thoughts start to intrude on your concentration, take yourself back to your breathing and the word 'rah'. Force out those distractions and try not to follow them.

Meditate for five minutes at a time until you find it easy to clear your mind of all distractions. With sufficient practice you will gradually be able to increase your meditation time for up to twenty minutes. If you can set aside a specific time every day to go through this technique it will more than repay itself in terms of the potential benefits. The best time to do it is first thing in the morning or last thing at night. As Gandhi said, 'Meditation is the key to the morning and the latch to the evening.'

How Meditation Works

Basically there are two sides to the brain and each has different functions, as illustrated below. In simple terms, the left side of the brain governs logic, analysis and word ability. The right side of the brain governs creativity and fantasy, picture images, lateral thought and imagination. Unless you are meditating it is only possible to use one side of the brain at a time. The left side of the brain normally dominates our consciousness, and when we repeat the one-word mantra during meditation we occupy the left brain with the monotonous job of concentrating on this. When we deliberately bring our attention back to the focal device and away from all other distractions, the right side of the brain then takes over, which results in a reduction in the stress response and a surge in our ability to relax. We feel a sense of tranquillity and of serenity. This is borne out by recordings of brainwave activity during meditation which show the characteristic alpha rhythms closely associated with rest.

Just like progressive and deep muscular relaxation, meditation can be practised anywhere suitable. However, anybody suffering from epilepsy or organic psychiatric disorders such as schizophrenia should consult their doctor before attempting meditation.

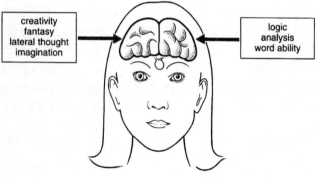

creativity
fantasy
lateral thought
imagination

logic
analysis
word ability

The two sides of the brain

Yoga

Yoga is another art which is based on an ancient Indian philosophy, and which has gained tremendous popularity in recent years in the West. This too is a good relaxation technique to calm the mind and reduce tension. Some of the exercises also bring about physical benefits, including improved flexibility, co-ordination and balance, whilst promoting muscle strength and endurance at the same time. In hatha yoga you practice co-ordinated movements and postures, called 'asanas', which exercise almost every area of the body combined with breath control techniques known as 'pranayamas'. In siddha yoga the concentration is on meditation techniques. For the correct type of yoga for you, and this has to be chosen carefully, the Yoga for Health Foundation or the British Wheel of Yoga can offer good advice.

Massage

Although the meaning of the word massage is often misunderstood, thanks to the tacky misuse of the word by the sex industry, physical massage is now available in many GP surgeries and hospital clinics. It is increasingly thought to be of benefit in treating a whole range of physical and emotional disorders. It is a powerful relaxation technique which is wonderfully comforting and which engenders a strong feeling of well-being, not only in the recipient but also in the person providing the massage. Foot and facial massage are good examples of the applications of therapeutic massage. The best source of bona fide therapeutic massage are chartered physiotherapists whose qualifications have been validated by a central agency, or else somebody approved by the British Massage Therapy Council. These organisations can provide lists of practitioners near you.

If you want to teach yourself massage, make sure that the skin is free of infection or inflammation and that whatever pain you have is not made worse, or does not spread to other areas, when pressure is applied. Then follow these steps.

1. Use a warm, quiet, dark room where there are no distractions.

2. Remove any watches or jewellery that could scratch the skin.

3. Expose the area to be massaged.

4. The person being massaged should lie on a firm, padded surface.

5. Ideally, use an aromatherapy massage oil so that your hands can glide smoothly over the skin. A light vegetable oil or talcum powder will do otherwise.

6. Pour no more than one teaspoonful of the massage oil into the palm of one hand and warm the oil up by rubbing your hands together.

7. Begin with circular movements, moulding your hands to the shape of the body and keeping a constant rhythm.

8. Always keep one hand in contact with the skin at all times. If more oil is needed, pour a little on to the back of the massaging hand and continue stroking as you use your other hand to transfer the extra oil on to the recipient's skin.

9. Keep conversation to a minimum during the massage.

10. On small areas, only use thumbs and fingertips.

11. On large areas, use the whole hand and firmer pressure.

12. If massage causes tickling, either increase the pressure or go on to a different part.

13. If muscle tension is being treated, your thumbs should exert deep pressure, moving in small circles.

14. To release tension in muscles around the shoulder or pelvic girdle and thighs, a kneading technique can be used which involves pummelling with the edge of the hand to create a chopping, bouncy effect on the muscles.

Personal Forms of Relaxation

There are many different ways of relaxing in addition to the practices outlined above. Early findings from a study conducted by the Institute of Management showed that some of the more unusual ways that managers chose to relax included growing apples, playing the bagpipes and flying helicopters. They also listed enjoying aromatherapy or hypnosis, biofeedback techniques, gardening, tai chi, shiatsu and reflexology. One-time Editor of *Cosmopolitan*, Marcelle D'Argy Smith, and business troubleshooter, Sir John Harvey-Jones, enjoy transcendental meditation. David Campbell, Chief Executive of Virgin Radio, gets away from it all in his helicopter. Gareth Thompson, Chief Executive of the PR agency Hunt Thompson, grows apples at his home in Kent and uses the journey to the station every day in a beat-up old Land Rover as a therapeutic stress buster.

Some organisations have even got into the spirit of things by adopting some of the principles of feng shui, a three-thousand-year-old Oriental philosophy which holds that the positioning of furniture and the species of plants in the working environment can promote health and industry. I am told that Marks and Spencer and the mobile phone network Orange are great advocates of this. So much so that at Orange's Bristol headquarters it has been said that the office furniture is skilfully positioned so as to avoid blocking energy lines.

At the end of the day it does not matter what you think of these weird and wonderful philosophies pervading the last vestiges of die-hard British industry. Providing they reduce stress and enable people to work more productively and happily, then they must all be of benefit. Surely anything that does no harm is well worth a try?

CHAPTER SIXTEEN

IMPROVING YOUR LIFESTYLE

The way we live our lives can provide powerful physical defences against the ravages of the stress response. Ask yourself how stressful your life is by completing the questionnaire at the end of this chapter on page 205.

Since the stress response gears us up for the fight or flight reaction, only fighting or fleeing can truly neutralise the biological consequences. Exercise therefore is the only physical counter against stress. Unfortunately in the modern age of cars, escalators and lifts, far too few people take adequate levels of exercise, especially when fewer people are employed in manual jobs. We know from looking at the stress response in Chapter 3 that unchecked pressure is bad for us. A spring which is slowly wound up to maximum tension has to be released before it will spring back to a healthy state of rest. The human body is like this and it needs some kind of physical release to enable it to relax.

Benefits of Exercise

People who exercise regularly are generally more in tune with their bodies and how they feel and function. They are likely to be more aware of muscle tension, stiffness, and less fluidity of movement when exercise has not been taken for a while. People who are fitter through having taken regular activity often report the ability to think faster and more clearly. They feel better in themselves and have sharper, more acute reflexes. In fact, many feel so good that they go on to exercise too much. They spend inordinate amounts of time in the gym at the expense of their work and social life. This is because the neurotransmitters, endorphins, which are produced as a result of exercise are like natural opiates in the brain. They give the person a 'buzz' and a wonderful sense of euphoria.

Appropriate levels of exercise are incredibly beneficial. Just look at the following list to see what exercise can do for you.

- Lowers the risk of heart attacks and strokes.
- Lowers blood pressure.
- Lowers cholesterol.
- Reduces the risk of blood clots.
- Keeps the weight down.
- Prevents brittle bone disease (osteoporosis).
- Lessens the risk of premature death.
- Reduces the risk of diabetes.
- Improves mood, reduces anxiety and depression, and reduces stress.
- Improves quality of sleep.
- May lessen the risk of certain cancers.

Different kinds of exercise may be better for different kinds of stress. For fitness, three or four twenty-minute aerobic episodes of exercise every week are of maximum benefit. But for stress based on anger, for the tension caused by seething frustration and rage, probably more vigorous exercise, such as a hard session on the squash court, a cross-country run, kick boxing, or a workout in the gym, would be best. On the other hand if the stress is caused by bereavement, or from a relationship breakup, then the person needs nurturing and comfort and the body needs to be looked after. Some long warm baths, gentle stretching, yoga, long walks in the fresh air and massages are more likely to be helpful. For depression, activity incorporating social involvement such as class workouts, running groups and dancing are all recommended. For anxiety, any exercise which uses up the stress hormones noradrenalin and adrenalin are useful, so cycling, jogging, aerobics classes or swimming can restore a sense of self-worth and calm.

Remember that exercise should never be associated with torture or discomfort. For children it no longer means running round the school playground in the freezing cold wearing next to nothing. It should always be fun and it should always make you feel good. Whatever you do decide to do in the way of physical activity, remember these five essential guidelines.

1. Warm up before starting for at least five minutes with stretching exercises and jumping on the spot.

2. Don't go at it like a bull in a china shop. Build up your fitness slowly and make sure you exercise within the limits of your comfort. In time, you will be able to do more and more.

3. When you feel excessively tired stop and rest, your body is telling you something.

4. Cool down again after stopping the exercise and stretch to avoid stiffness.

5. Aim for a pace which keeps you moderately puffed and try and do both aerobic work and lightweight work. Three times a week for about twenty minutes is ideal.

Nutrition

Nutrition is important but is not worthy of obsession. If we were to believe everything we read in books with titles like *Eat Your Way to Health*, *Food for Life*, *The De-stress Diet*, *Detoxification Made Simple* and *The Complete Encyclopaedia of Nutritional Therapy*, it would be easy to believe that to become an Olympic athlete you would just have to go to the right restaurants all the time! It simply is not the case that you need to eat organic food all the time, or spend hundreds of pounds on food supplements extracted from the root of some little-known South American plant species. However, eating a well-balanced and varied diet containing as much wholesome natural food as possible certainly makes a difference to our well-being. With all of the many staple and exotic foodstuffs we have to choose from now, it is easy to obtain the right quantities of the essential ingredients from a good diet and it is quite possible to do this on a limited budget.

The good diet means a menu which is low in saturated fat which is otherwise turned into cholesterol by the body. It means eating most of our calorie intake in the form of carbohydrate which is our main energy source. It means eating a small but necessary amount of protein which we can either get from lean red meat or from nuts, dairy produce and pulses. It means eating plenty of fibre in the form of wholegrain cereals and fresh fruit and vegetables. It means cutting down on sugar and salt and choosing foods which are rich in vitamins and minerals but which are not damaged or destroyed in preparation or cooking. And once again, changing to a diet which is healthier can be fun. It is not an exercise just for masochists. A good diet makes you feel energetic and lively. It helps you keep in shape and cut the flab. It means good digestion and healthy skin. And, if we are to believe half of what the scientists are now telling us, it might even help us slow down the ageing process and reduce our risk of cancer in the future.

Moderation In Most Things

An eighty-eight-year-old man once told me in my consulting room that it was his birthday. He had never smoked, had never drank and had remained celibate all his life. So here he was, he said, ready to celebrate his eighty-eighth birthday. How, I asked myself, was he going to do it? The moral of the tale I suppose is that there should be moderation even in moderation. Taking anything to extremes is usually unhealthy. Teetotallers for example have been shown to have a higher rate of heart disease than people who drink in moderation. People who have a little flutter on the horses, or who try out exotic international cuisine, do themselves little harm. The occasional risk in life, the gamble, the odd pushing the boat out and chancing of the arm is probably quite good for the spirit. If we never give ourselves treats or enjoy special occasions, the rest of life becomes plain and dull. So looking after ourselves by way of the occasional reward and pat on the back is a good thing.

It is easy when we are stressed to rely on the false friends of alcohol and cigarettes, but even drinking large amounts of caffeinated coffee or tea can produce intense stimulation of the nervous system with the withdrawal symptoms of headaches and nausea when the intake slows. It is best to use these substances in moderation in our lives. If you want to remind yourself of the particular problems associated with them, look back to Chapter 11.

Getting Enough Sleep

A good night's sleep is something we all desperately need, and probably take for granted, yet without it we feel tired, unhappy, and grumpy. As many as one in five people suffers from sleeping problems of one sort or another. Insomnia accounts for about ten percent of all consultations with the doctor and, as the people affected know only too well, a fair amount of misery as well. But drastic measures are seldom necessary. You certainly don't need to move house, change jobs, take to the bottle or accept prescriptions for tranquillizers or sleeping tablets. This ten-step guide offers simple, easy-to-follow advice which should ensure anyone, however weary, gets a refreshing and well-deserved good night's sleep.

1. Go to bed at a reasonable time

Establishing a regular pattern of sleep helps the body to set its own synchronised inner clock which automatically encourages sleep. However, even the strictest routines are sometimes broken by unavoidable factors. Jet lag, shift working, family crises, and work commitments can all interfere with your usual timetable. At these times make sure you go to bed at an appropriate time. There is little point turning in if you are not yet feeling in the least bit tired, but by the same token, avoid working until you are literally fit to drop. Most of us have experienced the frustration of ending up so exhausted that natural sleep just refuses to come, with a restless night of tossing and turning to follow. Good sleep calls for good timing, so go to bed at a regular, reasonable time every night and give sleep a chance.

2. Avoid eating too late at night

Eating late means indigestion and heartburn are highly likely. A full stomach also stimulates the intestine and produces extra body heat and sweating, which many people find uncomfortable. The tick-over speed of the body also increases, so awareness of your heartbeat or an audible pulsation through your ear on the pillow is noticeable. Late night eating will do your waistline no good either, as the energy produced by digesting the food will not be utilised while you sleep, and will be converted directly to fat. Try eating a smaller, unhurried meal earlier in the evening, and avoid that late night take-away, or highly calorific TV snack.

3. Avoid excessive smoking and drinking in the evening

Smoking is a stimulant and excites the nervous system, the very part of you which has to relax in order for you to get to sleep. Although you may think it is helping you to relax and unwind at the end of a busy day, smoking will actually do just the opposite. Conversely, alcohol is a depressant. It may make you sleepy and tired at first, so that you drop off to sleep quickly, but it has the distinct disadvantage of waking you up again halfway through the night when your body has overcome the alcohol's effects, and when you need to empty your bladder. Since your body quickly becomes used to alcohol, you become increasingly likely to sleep badly in the future. Regular drinking to help you get off to sleep is a dangerous and ineffective habit to start.

4. Avoid other hidden stimulants

For centuries caffeine in coffee and tea has commonly been drunk to keep people awake, so it is hardly surprising that it is not recommended for insomniacs. Cola drinks, red wine, chocolate and cheese also contain stimulants, as do many drugs and medicines. Ask your doctor if anything you are currently prescribed could be keeping you awake. Appetite suppressants, asthma inhalers, certain pain killers and anti-depressants are among the commonest.

5. Take regular daily exercise
We all know that physical exercise is generally healthy, but on a regular basis it has been shown to improve the quality of sleep too, partly by influencing hormone secretion in the brain itself. Exercise tires you physically as well as mentally, but remember to give yourself plenty of time to recover properly from its invigorating effects before settling down to sleep. Daytime exertion is therefore always preferable. Things like swimming, cycling, jogging, brisk walking, and racquet sports are ideal.

6. Make sure the bedroom is dark and quiet
A noisy room without blinds or curtains would be a total nightmare, if you could get to sleep in the first place! Many people do actually need less sleep in the summer because they are aroused by the long hours of daylight. Extraneous noises like traffic, loud music, babies crying, and other people's snoring can also prove highly disturbing. It is not always possible to sleep in optimal surroundings, but mini-mise distractions by fitting dark curtains or blinds, keep doors closed, and consider using ear plugs, which are available from most chemists.

7. Make sure the bedroom is warm but well-ventilated
When your body is cold it sends primitive survival messages to your brain stopping you from sleeping, so adequate covers on the bed are obviously important. Although being 'snug as a bug in a rug' is one thing, a little circulating fresh air is helpful

for refreshing sleep. It is very easy to feel uncomfortable as a result of being too hot and stuffy, and starved of oxygen. Be warm, but also keep the air fresh.

8. Establish a sleeping routine
Most of us are creatures of habit, but never more so than when it comes to sleeping. Going to bed at the same time each night establishes a pattern to which our bodies become inevitably accustomed. A regular routine of, say, an early meal, watching TV, a hot milky drink, then retiring to bed at a given time with a relaxing book seldom fails to work. If dropping off to sleep is the problem, don't make the mistake of lying in for longer the next morning. Set the alarm to wake you a little earlier each morning, and avoid taking naps during the day, so that you are relatively more tired and more likely to fall asleep quickly the following night. This then becomes your routine.

9. Relax just before going to bed
Just like a car travelling at 100mph which needs time to brake to a standstill, so your mind needs time to fully unwind. You cannot work all day without a break and then fall into a deep refreshing sleep as if by magic. Some gentle music, quiet reading, yoga or other relaxation technique may be useful, as well as unwinding peacefully with your partner and family. It is worth setting aside up to two hours at the end of the day before going to bed.

10. A comfortable bed
None of the above advice is much good unless you have a comfortable bed to sleep on, especially if back problems, joint pains, neck stiffness or pregnancy are preventing you sleeping. A good supportive bed-base and mattress are perhaps the best investments you can ever make for your

health, especially since you will spend so many hours of your life asleep. The bed needs to correctly support the body to prevent backache and stop you rolling in towards your partner, or rolling off towards the edge, which can be so disruptive to restful sleep. When choosing your new bed and mattress, take your sleeping partner with you, and don't be embarrassed to both try lying on the bed to assess its suitability. Remember, we are all individuals with different requirements for comfort and support. Listen to expert advice, and make sure you are both happy with the bed you choose.

A good night's sleep is essential for enabling you to carry on a busy schedule and a healthy lifestyle. I believe there are very few people with sleeping problems who could not identify at least one or two things in this guide which they could change for the better. Have another look at the guide, and sleep on it. Pleasant dreams!

Questionnaire: How Stressful
is Your Lifestyle?

For each of the statements below choose the number which most accurately reflects where you stand in terms of your lifestyle on a typical day. Award yourself a point from 1 to 10. For example, on the first statement, if you eat saturated fat at every meal every day give yourself 10 points, but if you eat it only occasionally award yourself 1 point. Then do the same for all 20 statements

1	I keep my saturated fat intake to a minimum	1 2 3 4 5 6 7 8 9 10	I eat fatty food at most meals
2	I choose foods rich in fibre	1 2 3 4 5 6 7 8 9 10	I go for fast food generally
3	I make a point of drinking plenty of water	1 2 3 4 5 6 7 8 9 10	I never drink just water
4	I generally eat breakfast	1 2 3 4 5 6 7 8 9 10	I usually skip breakfast
5	I always have fresh fruit and vegetables at home	1 2 3 4 5 6 7 8 9 10	Most fruit and vegetables I eat are tinned
6	I hardly ever miss meals	1 2 3 4 5 6 7 8 9 10	I often miss meals
7	I take a multivitamin supplement most days	1 2 3 4 5 6 7 8 9 10	I never waste money on vitamins
8	I avoid too many strong, caffeinated drinks	1 2 3 4 5 6 7 8 9 10	I need strong coffee and other drinks to wake me up
9	I drink within the 'safe' recommended limits for alcohol	1 2 3 4 5 6 7 8 9 10	I regularly exceed the 'safe' recommended alcohol limits
10	I never binge on alcohol and get 'legless'	1 2 3 4 5 6 7 8 9 10	I often sink a few drinks too many and suffer hangovers
11	I never drink every day	1 2 3 4 5 6 7 8 9 10	I always drink every day
12	I do not miss a drink if I do not have one	1 2 3 4 5 6 7 8 9 10	I really need and crave a drink most days
13	I do not smoke, and never have done	1 2 3 4 5 6 7 8 9 10	I regularly smoke
14	None of my family and few of my friends smoke	1 2 3 4 5 6 7 8 9 10	I'm surrounded by other people who smoke

15	I exercise for at least half an hour three times a week	1 2 3 4 5 6 7 8 9 10	I last exercised when I left school
16	I'd rather walk up two or three flights of stairs than take the lift	1 2 3 4 5 6 7 8 9 10	I'll always take the lift if it's there
17	My work entails a fair amount of physical exercise	1 2 3 4 5 6 7 8 9 10	My job is sedentary
18	My weight is just right for my height	1 2 3 4 5 6 7 8 9 10	I'm very overweight for my height
19	I enjoy a regular sleep routine	1 2 3 4 5 6 7 8 9 10	I grab some sleep when I'm not burning the candle at both ends
20	I make exercise a priority and do it even if I'm tired mentally	1 2 3 4 5 6 7 8 9 10	I'll always put off exercise if I'm too tired

Self-assessment

The higher your score in this questionnaire the less healthy a lifestyle you are leading. Each high-scoring answer increases your vulnerability to stress, even though you may be adopting certain habits in the mistaken belief that they are helping you cope with stress.

Above 140 points

With the lifestyle you are leading, you are heading for an early grave! You may not be aware of it now, but the way you are living will be taking its toll on you. Many of the early warning signs of stress which you will exhibit are being made worse by what you are doing to yourself. Take steps to change things now.

90–140 points

This is better, but there is still no room for complacency. Any increase in unfavourable life events, or in stresses at work or at home, and your lifestyle could easily take an unhealthy turn for the worse. Get into regular healthy habits and make exercise and leisure a priority.

Below 90 points

Well done! Your lifestyle is a healthy one and gives you the best possible chance of being able to cope with all the hassles and pressures of life to your best advantage. You will also be more in tune with your body and be able to react more quickly if your stress levels build up.

CHAPTER SEVENTEEN

LOVE AND LAUGHTER

Giving and Receiving Love

When people feel secure, supported and loved they are much more likely to stay healthy and happy than people who are insecure and live in isolation. Married people generally live longer and enjoy better health than those who are single, and when we think about the effects of the stress hormones it is easy to understand why. People who are able to share their problems with others and can discuss their difficulties and hardships know the value of dissipating their stress this way. Their levels of noradrenalin, adrenalin and cortisol are lowered and all of the damaging physical consequences of tension and dread ease away. But it is not just the love and support that we get from our closest partner which is important, we also need respect and affection from friends and work colleagues. The adage 'a problem shared is a problem halved' certainly holds true. There is also the therapeutic value that other people experience when listening to somebody else's woes and helping to put them right. Giving love as well as receiving it is vital to all of us.

From the Cradle to the Grave

From our very early childhood, we all crave to be cradled in the arms of our parents and to be cuddled, kissed and hugged as every new experience we face is a threat and a challenge. A childhood devoid of love, or where love and respect are not given unconditionally, will often lead to difficulties in adult life later, such as being unable to form healthy interpersonal and sexual relationships, poor parenting and drug abuse. In our adult lives we should be able to savour the joy of all our senses, not only the sight of beautiful things and the aroma and taste of wonderful food, but also the pleasure of touching, caressing and stroking, which are a natural and intrinsic part of forming lasting personal bonds.

Pet Therapy

The benefits of stroking and of sharing love are even borne out in scientific trials surrounding pet therapy. Bringing in carefully selected and suitable animals to hospital wards has not only been shown to improve patient morale considerably, but has actually reduced the recurrence rate of heart attack in people admitted to coronary care units. Stroking a furry animal actually reduces the blood pressure. We all know there are guide-dogs for the blind but there are also dogs which can assist the deaf. Studies have shown that people suffering from depression and anxiety, people living in isolation, and the elderly who no longer have a close companion, can all derive tremendous emotional benefit from owning or just being visited by a pet. Even aggressive young offenders in prisons have experienced behavioural modification as a result of being visited by domestic animals. The charity known as CHATA, The Children in

Hospital and Animal Therapy Association, regularly visits the children's wards at the Queen Elizabeth Hospital, Hackney and Great Ormond Street in order to entertain the children there and distract them from some of the clinical goings-on around them.

Self-Love

Whilst we can give love to pets we still need to receive love from other people, and we need to be fond of ourselves too. Here are some simple steps that can pave the way to feeling good and having a positive outlook.

1. When under pressure, try not to be harshly critical of yourself but instead be loving and caring. Develop some positive and affirming statements to counter some of your major self-criticisms.

2. Compliment yourself when you do well and concentrate on your strengths rather than your weaknesses.

3. Pick some everyday situations and make a note of your positive and pessimistic attitudes towards them. If the pessimistic ones seem to be more heavily weighted think of some positive opposite statements, and then practise them in other situations.

4. Stop seeing yourself as a victim of the system, or your company, or the people around you. You know you have the power to change this.

5. Identify those things which you value in your life and the things which you stand for, and concentrate on them.

6. Identify the people you feel closest to and think of ways of strengthening those relationships.

7. Whenever you feel upset, make a habit of talking to somebody you trust and be conscious of how you feel afterwards.

8. Always ask yourself where your feelings are coming from and what you would like to see changed.

9. Express these feelings clearly and respectfully to the other person. Seek the other's point of view and negotiate a plan of action.

10. Buy a gift or write a letter for somebody you like.

11. Spend more time with the children.

12. Give others praise and recognition for jobs well done. People are much more likely to co-operate with you and respond to you if you do.

Spend More Time With Your Children

Spending more time with your children is a great remedy for excessive stress and a marvellous exercise in giving and receiving unconditional love. But children can be a source of stress in themselves, as well as needing the love, support and encouragement of a parent. Since so many of the adult sources of stress stem from childhood experiences and environment, it really is important to provide your own children with a stable, secure and loving background. They have anxieties and sources of stress too. Starting at a new school, the rivalry of a brother or sister, insecurity generated by parental separation or arguments, and the enormous stress of examinations. So remember to praise your child when they do something well. Try to phrase your requests in a positive way such as, 'I would really like you to put your toys away tidily,' rather than, 'Clear up this dreadful mess.'

Remember there is a big difference between children's behaviour that you do not like and behaviour which is socially unacceptable, like pulling hair, kicking or biting. With younger children who are behaving badly, distract them and show your disapproval. With older ones, explain why it is that what they are doing cannot be tolerated. Try to avoid slapping your child, especially when you are angry. Better to withhold a treat or to send them to bed early than to resort to any physical punishment. Criticise a child's behaviour, but not the child. Harsh words and threats can be almost as damaging in the long term as any kind of corporal punishment. Remember that childhood does not last forever and it is well worth enjoying all the good things about it whilst you can. Remember also that you are the most important person in the child's life. They love you and it is important that you remind them how much you love them. Get as much help as you can when the going gets tough and remember that a happy parent makes for a happy child. Reserve some time just for yourself and treat yourself occasionally to something special. That way you will be able to listen to your children as little people rather than just hearing them and not being able to give them the opportunity to develop and grow.

The Stress-Relieving Properties of Humour

Whilst I was working on this book, a friend sent me the 'stress relief kit' illustrated overleaf. It had the desired effect, it made me laugh. Yes, it broke my concentration for a few minutes and yes, it is hugely cynical, but it brightened my day and afforded a moment of total freedom from being too serious. Many people take life too seriously and have forgotten how to smile. We all know what it is like to have a sense of humour failure and it is not much fun. Our mind is set on remaining irritated, annoyed and angry and at such moments absolutely nothing seems funny any more. But happiness, humour and laughter have a powerful influence on life and healing. This has been recognised in many of the most ancient cultures, from Greece to North East Asia and South America. Many of today's leading doctors see humour as an effective antidote to stress, and there are now NHS 'laughter clinics' established in Britain.

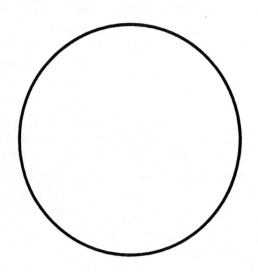

hit head hard in circle

stop to see if stress is relieved

if stress relief is not achieved repeat until you become unconscious

Stress relief kit

A genuine smile, involving the mouth, eyes and heart, relaxes facial muscles and is thought to increase the blood flow to the brain. It takes much more energy and effort to contort and constrict facial features into a frown or grimace. Smiling reduces irritation, anger and hostility and seems contagious to others. It is a wonderful tool in diffusing difficult or awkward situations. 'Laugh and the whole world laughs with you', as the saying goes. The British Safety Council, who organise the Smile for Safety Week, reveal that humour and happiness in the workplace can reduce the prevalence of industrial accidents and raise productivity and performance. Some studies have even shown scientific evidence that happy laughter can raise immunity and protect against disease and malignancy. The most recent work confirms that people who regularly use laughter, humour and play as coping mechanisms for everyday situations have a significantly higher count of immune cells than others. So the bottom line is that laughter really could be the best medicine of all.

If you like a joke, make sure you enjoy one and share it with those around you. If you yourself want to be happy then spread a little happiness about you. After all, if you want love you have to give it as well as receive it. Finally, remember that the way you laugh can tell other people a great deal about your personality. The person who laughs too much and too loudly can be every bit as bad as the person who doesn't laugh at all. And people who laugh at other people rather than with them tend to be unhappy, rather unconfident people who use humour to be derisory and hostile. To be able to laugh with others and at oneself demonstrates good self-esteem, strength of character, a healthy ego and bags of confidence. Spontaneous laughter is pleasant, infectious and stress-relieving.

CHAPTER EIGHTEEN

PROFESSIONAL HELP

It is all very well trying to learn how to cope with stress oneself or with the love, support and concern of other people, but there are thousands of people in this world who, for various reasons, find it difficult to talk to other people and who are lonely and isolated. That isolation may be an inextricable part of the problem. There may be no social network offering friendship, or a fear of rejection which prevents the first approach. Fortunately there are many sources of help available and the earlier assistance is sought the better. So who can you turn to if there are no immediate family or friends with whom to share your problems?

Outside the NHS

There are many voluntary bodies, such as the Samaritans and MIND, who can provide a sympathetic ear, advice and information. There will always be local voluntary groups in an area near you, such as the local branch of Relate, if the sources of stress are to do with relationships. Some people who have spiritual or religious beliefs may find solace and support from their faith, and many ministers of religion are highly experienced in dealing with the myriad sources of human stress.

Medical Help

The first port of call for most people seeking professional
help would be the family doctor or GP. They can often
suggest the solution themselves, perhaps arranging to see the
patient a few more times for review and to ensure the
satisfactory outcome of any counselling or treatment. But
in some cases, where insufficient time is available to the busy
GP or where the problem is persistent and severe, referral to
clinical psychologists, psychiatrists and psychotherapists is
perfectly feasible. There are also such things as self-referral
clinics where it is not necessary to see the GP first, and
information on these is available from your local Community
Health Council, Citizens Advice Bureau, social services
department, library or community centre. Unfortunately,
limited NHS resources mean these clinics are few and far
between. The Mental Health Foundation's directory, *Someone to Talk To*, lists many other groups that can be
approached.

The GP

Family doctors are well-versed in all the trials and tribulations
of life which can detrimentally affect people and their health.
They also tend to know their patients, their patients' families
and their background reasonably well. For a start they can just
listen, which for many people is sufficient unburdening of
their woes. At the very least the GP can make a quick
assessment of the duration, severity and likely consequences
of the symptoms, and can carry out relevant examinations and
investigations. Whatever the GP chooses to instigate as the
next therapeutic step, they can at least run through the various

non-medical and complementary self-help techniques for handling everyday stress and tension.

Counselling

Most health care professionals, by offering reassurance, explanations, encouragement and sympathy are well used to providing emotional support and counselling to patients. The basic aim is to help people live the lives they have willingly chosen and to get them to understand the effects of any life events on themselves, their family or their situation. This means exploring the emotional and practical realities. A counsellor should encourage you to express your true feelings and emotions, irrational or not, and take you back through all the circumstances leading up to any crisis. They should examine all the implications and encourage the client to work out for themselves suitable new directions and decisions in life.

Counsellors vary in the techniques they use and, of course, in their personality and experience as well. Registered and qualified counsellors near you can be found by contacting the British Association of Counselling. The main qualities a client requires are sympathetic understanding, emotional warmth and sincerity.

Psychotherapy

Any treatment for a psychological condition, including stress, which does not rely on physical methods like electro-convulsive therapy or medication, comes under the umbrella description of psychotherapy.

The most important part of this treatment involves talking – communicating and listening to problems and then trying to redirect anger, frustration or anti-social behaviour in more appropriate ways. It can often identify the seeds of current problems in deep-seated and long-forgotten difficulties from childhood, in which case strategies can be developed to overcome these troublesome barriers to personal growth and development. Most psychotherapeutic approaches are based on the notion that difficulties arising from interpersonal relationships are a major contributor to stress and depression. This type of therapy therefore concentrates on the client's emotions involved in their close relationships, and focuses on their family, their friends, their work and their attitudes to society in general.

Like counselling, there are many different kinds of psychotherapy but perhaps the most useful is the 'cognitive' approach where the therapist aims to encourage the client to alter unhelpful ways of thinking, in other words to start learning from experience. But there are other types, including family therapy, group therapy, behavioural therapy and psychoanalysis. The type which any individual will derive most benefit from can only be determined by their particular circumstances.

Just talking to people can be therapeutic in itself, like the passing of time. It is a weight off your shoulders and a welcome emotional catharsis. Self-help groups work exceedingly well in much the same way, by bringing like-minded people with similar problems together so that they can enjoy safety in numbers. In a self-help group you are all in the same boat, and know beyond any doubt that, despite your worst fears, you really are not the only one in the world suffering from a particular problem.

CHAPTER NINETEEN

THE TOP FIFTY QUICK-FIX TIPS FOR BEATING STRESS

Fifty Tips for Beating Stress

1. Keep count of your life events.

2. Spend more time on those neglected hobbies.

3. Practise relaxation techniques.

4. Make a long-term life plan.

5. Learn to delegate.

6. Spend more time with family and friends.

7. Allow yourself time to unwind.

8. Cut back on fatty food.

9. Avoid perfectionism.

10. Establish your priorities.

11. Stay within sensible drinking limits.

12. Put social time for yourself in your appointment diary.

13. Ensure you are in the right job.

14. Do one job at a time and finish it.

15. Hug somebody regularly.

16. Enjoy a walk-break every day.

17. Accept your own faults and weaknesses.

18. Avoid setting unnecessary deadlines.

19. Smile more.

20. Be realistic about your goals and ambitions.

21. Cut your caffeine intake.

22. Accept other people's faults and weaknesses.

23. Speak and walk more slowly.

24. Seek help from others when you need it.

25. Organise your day to day activity more constructively.

26. Buy someone a gift.

27. Practise anger control using the quieting reflex.

28. Write to a friend.

29. Write down any outstanding jobs in a list to free your mind.

30. Leave your watch off on Sundays.

31. Think positively.

32. Snack on healthy foods, not junk foods.

33. Be more assertive.

34. Eliminate time-wasters from your life.

35. Practice mental rehearsal to prepare you for difficult situations.

36. Don't be forced to make on-the-spot decisions.

37. Cut interruptions and distractions to a minimum.

38. Handle phone calls on your own terms, call back if necessary.

39. Re-schedule appointments to coincide with times when you feel at your best.

40. Don't bother getting angry about things you cannot change.

41. Laugh and play more every day.

42. Take regular fun exercise.

43. Cut back or give up smoking.

44. Communicate stress by sharing it with a friend or associate whom you trust.

45. In crisis meetings, handle the emotions first, think about the content later.

46. Take a 'nice person' break. When under pressure find someone who lifts your spirits to spend time with.

47. Keep things in perspective. How serious is the situation really?

48. Move on when you've done your best. Don't dwell and linger on something when there is nothing more you can do.

49. Practise being a good listener.

50. Finally, praise and encourage others when they've done well.

USEFUL ADDRESSES

GREAT BRITAIN:

AA
General Service Office
PO Box 1
Stonebow House
Stonebow
York YO1 2NJ
Tel admin: 01904 644026
Helpline 10am–10pm:
0171 352 3001

ACCEPT (Alcohol related)
724 Fulham Road
London SW6 5SE
Tel 0171 371 7477

Al-ANON helpline
61 Great Dover Street
London SE1 4YF
Tel 0171 403 0888

ACTION FOR VICTIMS OF
MEDICAL ACCIDENTS
Bank Chambers
1 London Road
Forest Hill
London SE23 3TP
Tel 0181 291 2793

ASH
109 Gloucester Place
London W1H 3PH
Tel 0171 935 3519

ASSOCIATION FOR POST-NATAL
ILLNESS
25 Jerdan Place
London SW6 1BE
Tel 0171 386 0868

BRITISH ASSOCIATION OF
CANCER UNITED PATIENTS
(BACUP)
121-123 Charterhouse Street
London EC1M 6AA
Freephone Mon–Thur:
0800 181199

BRITISH ASSOCIATION FOR
COUNSELLING
1 Regent Place
Rugby CV21 2PJ
Tel 01788 550899

BRITISH MASSAGE THERAPY
COUNCIL
3 Woodhouse Cliff
Headingley
Leeds
W. Yorkshire LS6 2HF

BRITISH WHEEL OF YOGA
1 Hamilton Place
Boston Road
Sleaford NG34 7ES
Tel 01529 306851

CHATA (CHILDREN IN HOSPITAL
AND ANIMAL THERAPY
ASSOCIATION)
Tel 0181 445 7883

DIVORCE CONCILIATION AND
ADVISORY SERVICE
38 Ebury Street
London SW1W OLU
Tel 0171 730 2422

FAMILIES NEED FATHERS
National Administration Centre
134 Curtain Road
London EC2A 3AR
Tel 0171 613 5060

GAMBLERS ANONYMOUS
PO Box 88
London SW6 3DO
Helpline 0171 384 3040

INSTITUTE OF PSYCHOSEXUAL
MEDICINE
11 Chandos Street
London W1M OEB

ISSUE (NATIONAL FERTILITY
ASSOCIATION)
509 Aldridge Road
Great Barr
Birmingham B44 8NA
Tel 1021 3444414

MANIC DEPRESSION
FELLOWSHIP
8-10 High Street
Kingston-Upon-Thames KT1 1EY
Tel 0181 974 6550

MIND
Granta House
15-19 Broadway
London E15 4BQ
Tel 0181 519 2122
Helpline 10–12 noon, 2–4.30pm:
0181 522 1728

NATIONAL ASSOCIATION FOR
BEREAVEMENT
122 Whitechapel High Street
London E1 7PT
Tel 0171 247 1080

NEXUS
Tel 0181 367 6328

ORGANISATION FOR PARENTS
UNDER STRESS
Tel 01702 559900

PHOBIC ACTION
Claybury Grounds
Manor Road
Woodford Green
Essex 1G8 8PR
Tel 0181 559 2551
Helpline 0181 559 2459

RELATE
Herbert Gray College
Little Church Street
Rugby CV21 3AP
Tel 01788 573241

RELAXATION FOR LIVING TRUST
29 Burwood Park Road
Walton-on-Thames
Surrey KT12 5LH

REPETITIVE STRAIN INJURY
ASSOCIATION
Chapel House
152-156 High Street
Yiewsley
West Drayton
Middx
Tel 01895 431134

THE SAMARITANS
10 The Grove
Slough
Berks SL1 1QP
Tel 01753 532713

THE STANDING CONFERENCE
ON DRUG ABUSE (SCODA)
Waterbridge House
32-6 Loman Street
London SE1 OEE
Tel 0171 928 9500

TRANSCENDENTAL MEDITATION
(TM)
Roydon Hall
East Beckham
Nr. Tonbridge
Kent TN12 5HN
Tel 0800 269303

YOGA THERAPY CENTRE
Royal London Homeopathic
Hospital
Great Ormond Street
London WC1N 3HR
Tel 0171 833 7267

CANADA:
ADDICTION RESEARCH
FOUNDATION
33 Russell Street
Toronto M5S 2S1
Tel 1 416 595 6000
Fax 1 416 595 5017

ALANON FAMILY GROUPS
1712 Avenue Road, Box 54533
North York M5M 4N5
Tel 1 416 366 4072

ALCOHOLICS ANONYMOUS
234 Eglinton Avenue E., Suite 202
Toronto M4P 1K5
Tel 1 416 487 5591
Fax 1 416 487 5855

CANADIAN CANCER SOCIETY
Metropolitan Toronto Region
77 Bloor Street W., Suite 1702
Toronto M5S 3A1
Tel 1 416 975 5585
Fax 1 416 975 5393

CLARKE INSTITUTE OF
PSYCHIATRY
250 College Street
Toronto M5T 1R8
Tel 1 416 979 2221
Fax 1 416 979 6902

DISTRESS CENTRE
INCORPORATED
Box 243, Adelaide PO
Toronto M5C 2J4
Tel 1 416 598 1121

ELIBAY'S RELAXATION
Responce Institu
2221 Yonge Street, Suite 503B
Toronto, ON, M4S 2B4
Tel 1 416 932 2784

HEART AND STROKE
FOUNDATION OF ONTARIO
477 Mount Pleasant Road, 4th
Floor
Toronto M4S 2L9
Tel 1 416 489 7100
Fax 1 416 489 9015

STRESS MANAGEMENT "TRAIN
THE TRAINER"
Wellness Innovations Newwork
Corp.
Jan Shepard
Tel 1 416 955 9323
Fax 1 416 955 9320

TORONTO NATUROPATHIC
CLINIC
180 Bloor Street W., Suite 607
Toronto, ON, M5S 2V6
Tel 1 416 944 3526

TORONTO WELLNESS CENTRE
22 Wellesley Street W.
Tel 1 416 920 2722

INDEX

Numbers in italics refer to figures.